THE MEN AT THE GATE

THE MEN AT THE GATE

by

OTTIERO OTTIERI

translated by I. M. Rawson

LONDON
VICTOR GOLLANCZ LTD
1962

Printed in Great Britain by
The Camelot Press Ltd., London and Southampton

TRANSLATOR'S NOTE

In writing the following account of his experiences in southern Italy, the author, who worked in the Olivetti factory there, has merely changed the names of places and characters. Santa Maria, Castello, etc., will not be found on the map, but apart from this the background and the incidents in the book are all true to life.

FOREWORD

Tomorrow, Monday, I start work.

Today my wife and I left the hotel on the sea-front at Santa Maria to move into the house we have taken on the hillside above Castello. As I came downstairs with our suitcases a man in a brown woollen singlet stepped forward and asked if he might speak to me, the manager of the new factory.

I said at once: "I am not the manager. I'm just an employee. And I've not yet begun work."

The man was in no way taken aback; it seemed that he did not believe me, or else thought that any member of our staff was as good as a manager. Tall, dignified, with light brown hair, he was ready with his enquiry: "Doctor, are you looking for a house?"

"I've found one. We're just going there."

"I can offer you one: a special opportunity. A big house in Via Dante . . ."

"Alighieri?"

"How is it that you know this street, Doctor?"

"I don't know the street. I know the name."

"The house would suit you, it's just the house for a manager."

"But I have a house and I'm not the manager. Please, let it be known here that I'm not the manager."

Still anxious to oblige, and gratified at my request, he bowed gravely and said, "I'll see to it, Doctor", as he picked up our suitcases and carried them to the waiting car. His woollen singlet was one of those that in our northern cities is usually worn in winter by the workers, under a shirt; it is almost a uniform here for the sub-proletariate, and he wore it proudly, like a cuirass, though it was full of holes.

I am not a manager. I am employed in the personnel office of the new factory built at Santa Maria by a famous manufacturing company of northern Italy. As a psychologist I shall be chiefly concerned with the selection of new workers, and in so doing I shall use "psychotechnical" methods, in other words, intelligence tests combined with individual interviews, with the aim of forming some estimate of the applicant's personality.

The factory has been functioning for a year or two, but work has started gradually and only now is the organization beginning to take shape. The managing staff is a small one, and each member of it undertakes various duties. The manager himself deals with the workers' representatives. The production-manager, an engineer, is directly responsible for the workers, each one of whom he knows individually. As to the personnel office, it has only just been set up, and will be entirely engaged with the problem of selection and of exterior relations: since almost the whole of the working class in this densely populated area has applied for jobs in the factory, which can take only three or four hundred and will not be expanding by more than another hundred or two. Not until these applications have been successfully dealt with will the personnel office, having earned the trust of the management, be able to assume responsibility for the well-being of the workers in the factory. For the present, the manager is the real head of the personnel.

The factory has arisen as a workshop, a department of the works in northern Italy. Instead of adding to these, a new building has been put up in the south, in the hope of relieving to some extent the unemployment there, or at least of throwing light upon the problems involved. It is not an ordinary workshop; the architect has designed one of the most beautiful factories in Europe, surrounded by a garden; with library, sick-rooms, welfare offices and dining-hall attached. A small world in itself, but one that is quickly striking root, both materially and spiritually, in Santa Maria.

The population of this southern land is a human mine, with the richest possibilities in the world. We have come to discover this unknown gold, which has been buried for so long by nature and by history.

CHAPTER I

MARCH. Monday

TODAY, FOR THE first time, I entered the factory's psycho-technical laboratory.

The candidates were seated at their desks, and raised their heads from their test-papers to look at me. Here's another of them, they were thinking, the latest arrival. What sort of man is he? Is his coming going to be a help to us, or not? They knew that the new member of the staff was one who would directly affect their own destinies. Bright sunlight flooded the room from the two glass walls at the corner, but I took off my dark glasses at once; all the same, I looked no one in the face, and maintained an impenetrable, official air. As a matter of fact, I hardly saw anybody, but, greeting Signorina S., my colleague, went at once to the table beside the blackboard and began to look through the candidates' application forms.

I was still pretending to be immersed in this occupation when the alarm clock on the table went off. Time was up for the written test with which the candidates were struggling. Signorina S., a tall north-erner, ordered them to stop what they were going, and we collected their papers while they shuffled on their chairs and stretched their limbs as though waking from sleep. The Signorina, having hurriedly given out new sheets of paper, began at once in her commanding voice to explain the next test.

This was a well-known method of discovering a candidate's non-verbal intellectual aptitudes, and consisted in a number of geometrical shapes which, printed all together at the bottom of the page, had to be mentally fitted into corresponding blank spaces in the upper half of the sheet of paper. Help from the fingers being impossible, this had to be done entirely by eye: a test to gauge not only a candidate's intelligence but in some measure also his mechanical ability, and one that involved various factors. For in so far as every test brings out one particular aspect of a man, so, in every aspect, the rest are comprehended. "Begin!" said the Signorina, and the heads of the unemployed applicants, fifteen of them, were bowed again over their papers.

Considerable zeal was to be observed. They struggled manfully in the endeavour mentally to transpose these natural shapes, without

the use of their hands. One could also note the birth of the Idea, of
the process of mental functioning, in the most remote depths of the
human mind. But after a while, as at school, one of them tried to crib
from another. A second raised a hand to ask for some useless explanation: forgetful of the alarm clock, with its allowance of three and a
half minutes, he was, it appeared, just taking his time. But the test
is one that depends on speed, and is not a matter of patience. A third
wanted to sharpen his pencil. Two of them did extremely well;
they had already finished and were gazing serenely at the ceiling.
On the other hand, a few gave up at once and left their papers blank.
In the meantime we had noticed one who, illiterate and unable to
hold his pencil properly—unable even to read the letters A, B, C,
etc., which had to be entered in the blank spaces—was intent on the
effort to fantasticate some kind of signature at the bottom of the page.
His cerebral matter was just not functioning at all.

The alarm clock sounded, and in imitation of the Signorina and
my former schoolmasters when written work was being done in
class, I said: "Hand in your papers."

They raised their heads again: boys and broad-shouldered men in
jackets or jerseys, some of them fishermen, together with towns-
men in dark suits, and even one girl—all stared at me once more as
though emptied of curiosity or anxiety; giving themselves up into
the hands of fate, before bending their heads again over the next test.

These written collective tests, which all had to take together—
there were to be individual tests in the afternoon, when each candidate
would be faced with some apparatus to tackle by hand—took the
whole morning. Some of them were designed to discover non-verbal
intellectual ability again; others for verbal knowledge and aptitude,
and receptivity; and others again for specific mechanical abilities,
where the candidate's skill is required to be of a more scholastic
nature. We corrected the papers as we went along, in order to waste
no time; ticking off the right answers and then awarding appropriate
marks according to a given code of evaluation. In other words, we
gave our suffrage to those we considered best. At times, not only I,
the newcomer, but also the Signorina, found our eyes drawn towards
the sea beyond the windows, or to a passing cart on the roadway.
This landscape, this panorama, seen from within the building where
our duty confines us, is like a beautiful face that one cannot help
turning to look at, surreptitiously, every now and then. There is a
fascinating luminous quality in the light clouds driven by the wind,
and in the reflections from the sea. Although I was supervising the

application of these tests in what was unknown ground to me, in southern Italy, my eyes were drawn again and again to the hills of Capo Alto across the bay, and to the wake of the distant sailing boats. But I was at once forced to restore my attention to the examination-room, where these grown-up pupils—these mature men and the pale-faced girl and the illiterate labourer—were all facing their day of judgment. The Signorina and I spoke briefly together in undertones, as those invigilating at examinations are wont to do when talking of their own affairs.

Tuesday

We carried on with the tests until 1 p.m. today. Their application is somewhat cursory down here, but in accordance with accepted practice. Perhaps in the room where they are held there is a lack of what the manuals of industrial psychology recommend: peace and quiet, comfort, and a sense of detachment from the world. But it may be that things are little different in every existing laboratory of the kind. There were still two women waiting and another illiterate, a big, heavy man.

When one o'clock struck we sent them all into the narrow corridor leading to the laboratory, and the Signorina and I stayed in the examination room, with the door closed. We were conscious of being behindhand. The Signorina pointed out that there was an endless number of applicants, and that the first group summoned for interviewing would take up all the week, including Sunday. "How many applications are there?" I asked.

"Oh, forty thousand. They're all filed. But we have to deal now with these candidates for examination."

"It would be better if they were all to do the individual tests, with the apparatus, this afternoon." The previous day we had only kept back those who had done sufficiently well in their written work for the later individual tests; the others had been sent away at once. "And then, I would like to speak to them all, one by one." In other words, I wanted those who had failed—and perhaps especially those—to come to the final interview, on which selection depended.

"How long do you want for each interview?" asked the Signorina.

"A quarter of an hour, perhaps half an hour."

"We must get through them all during the day. Many of them live far off, and can't come back. It will take us till midnight. The individual tests and the interviews are really only worth while for those who've passed the collective tests."

"But what about the others?"

"We give them their expenses and send them home, as we did yesterday."

I felt that we ought at least to see them singly, to hear what they had to say. "One can't rely only on the written tests," I said with scientific rather than humanitarian conviction.

"Do you want to speak to the ones who've left their papers blank, too?"

"Particularly with them . . ."

"Oh, well, of course you can see them all, if that's what you wish. It's up to you. But it's now a quarter past one, and I'm going to lunch. For months I've had cold meals, with these examinations."

The Signorina had given in, to let the newcomer try out his ideas, and find himself beating his head against a stone wall. We told the candidates that they could eat in the canteen, and must come back in the afternoon. At first they still crowded the corridor, uncertain what to do; then, breaking up into groups, some of them eager and others with a nonchalant air, they made their way to the canteen; for the most part, in good spirits. I rushed home in my car for a hurried meal with my wife in our small living-room, all windows, at the table on which I am writing this. It is dark now, and the shutters are closed. But by day, between one window opening on to the hillside and the other towards the sea, one feels suspended as though in a ship; the light is cold and clear, for the days are icy and the wind blows in through wide cracks in the window-frames. In our bedroom, where the big, white bed occupies three walls, we can hear the panes creaking as the branches of a carob-tree are beaten against them by the wind. The little house that we have taken is on a steep slope and almost overhangs the sea.

The candidates were waiting, and I drove back at full speed along the six kilometres of high road. Again we were confronted with the little group whose fate had inevitably to be decided during the day.

Many failed dismally at the individual tests: for the most part, they were those who had failed in the morning. At least it proved that the methods were consistent.

They could not fit the small steel pegs of the O'Connor apparatus into the holes in the board, using only one hand and timed by our chronometer. They found the Moede, a mechanical contrivance with wheels and levers that we took to pieces before their eyes, impossible to put together again; or produced so many suggestions and arguments that the whole afternoon would have been spent on it. In testing their manual co-ordination with the pantograph, with which, by means of two levers controlling a pencil point, they had to follow a curve traced on a sheet of paper, they nervously shot beyond the margins and made holes in the paper with the point. The Signorina was triumphant: "You see?" On the other hand, those who had done well in the morning at the verbal or non-verbal tests immediately showed manual skill, even if they had never been workers: it is always intelligence that counts, and, for us, intelligence must come before all else.

One of the two women, who had already done badly in the morning, was utterly defeated: although of delicate build and with slender fingers, she dropped the O'Connor pegs in her lap and would not go on with others available, as we urged her to do, but insisted on searching for the lost ones in her clothing or on the ground; and meanwhile the chronometer sounded inexorably. Her small head with its light-coloured hair drooped on to her shoulder almost as though her neck were broken. We had done our best to encourage her for fear she would burst into tears. Her dress was soaking at the armpits and the smell of the countrywoman was mingled with the sweaty odour of fear.

The illiterate applicant came next. With the coarse hands of a former manual worker he roughly seized the scattered pieces of the Moede apparatus and all but broke the transmission cord. "Look out!" cried the Signorina to us both. "If he breaks it, how am I to find another cord for the Moede?"

The man stopped for a moment, removed his heavy hands from our toy and raised his pock-marked visage, his eyes round with bewilderment. With lowered head he tried again, following the Signorina's directions, and, gently pulling the cord, slipped two of the cog-wheels on to the right bolts. His eyes gleamed with satisfaction, and he went boldly on; after the cog-wheels, he fitted the other pieces together anyhow, upside down or in the wrong order, while we maintained an astonished silence and the chronometer went on ticking. When he had finished, the fact that he had found a place for every piece seemed to him proof that he had succeeded. "Go on," said the Signorina, "now make it work."

He looked at us doubtfully. "Go on," said the Signorina, still waiting, an impenetrable expression on her face.

If the Moede is properly set, one should be able, by turning a wheel, to work a lever controlling a small hammer that beats on the floor of the mechanism; it is a cheerful sound, a sign of victory. He turned the wheel, but in vain; the lever could not work, every piece being wrongly mounted. He pushed harder, but the transmission was completely blocked. Using force, he tried once more.

"Stop! Stop! You'll smash it!" cried the Signorina. He put the apparatus from him, with a sombre look. "But I am a labourer. Try me out, but not with this. I can lift a hundredweight. I'm not afraid of anything. Put me in the factory and I'll do any work you like. What's the use of this thing?"

It was quietly explained to him that the experiment had been designed to test his mechanical skill in work resembling that of the factory.

"Mechanical, mechanical. But I am a heavy worker. I can do the work of three men. I'm not afraid of anything, even of what's mechanical."

I looked in his file for the form showing his date of birth, the number of his children, his schooling.

"Where have you worked before?"

"In the docks. I'm the best labourer at Santa Maria."

"But you see, we don't need manual workers."

"What is it you want, engineers?"

"Not engineers. Workers with mechanical skill."

"I've got the skill. Let me show you."

"This test was to show it."

"Oh, Doctor, so that was what it was. You might have told me before. I've never seen these things in factories. And I'm used to factories . . . I've been ten years in the dockyard. But I must work, I must eat."

"I see. What schooling have you had?"

"No schooling. My schooling's in my head. I like hard work." He struggled with a sense of angry shame. "I know my letters, they're in my head. I know my letters, and I have seven children, and I want to work hard. I must eat. I'll serve you better than all the rest," and he made a gesture towards the others beyond the door.

"Very well. Now go and wait outside."

He did not move.

"Go and wait in the corridor."

"Oh, I'm waiting. But what for, Doctor?"

"Just wait," I said kindly, hypocritically.

At last he went.

"Why was he called for the tests, if he is illiterate?"

"To convince him," said the Signorina. "Because it was simpler that way. For three months he's been waiting at the entrance, every morning. Look, we've still got ten to see, we must hurry." The tireder she gets, the more energetic the Signorina seems in her effort to catch up. She is a strong woman, and courageously bears the burden of this work of selection. But she added, with vexation: "The written tests were all we needed."

Meanwhile, the Manager was waiting in his office for the best of the candidates to be sent up, so that he could examine them rapidly himself, choose the *fine fleur*, and bring the working-day to an end. If we were to give each one an interview we should go on well into the night, and what should we be able to show for it? That an illiterate is a man like any other? It wasn't for me to pose as the expert who comes down from the north intending on his first day to reform southern Italy.

I told the Signorina that those who had passed the collective tests were to remain.

"And we're to send the others away?"

"Yes."

She breathed a deep sigh, as though of relief and regret.

"I'll call them in at once and pay them their expenses." She shouted the names in the corridor. They were alarmed and somewhat suspicious at this premature summons, since they saw that others were to remain. But those called in came and lined up before our table for a ritual that must have become well known in the vicinity. The Signorina announced officially: "We will now reimburse you for the day you have lost." Instead, it was all gain to them. They gave their names, we made out receipts for them to sign and we then handed over the money. For a moment they paused with it in their hands, and looked enquiringly at us.

"That's all for today. We will write to you."

Again an imperceptible query on each face, a slight shrug of the shoulders.

"That's all. You can go now."

They went, quietly, and as though taken unawares. One wondered why they should be so submissive. Perhaps because of the money? But who knows what goes on in their minds?

Friday

It is my job to write the final report on every candidate: a general summing-up, which is then filed, of the results of his tests and of the conclusions to be drawn from the interview. The latter is simply a talk between us. I try to seek out the infinitely varied aspects of the human personality (the personality of the worker presents as many problems as any other), and I check up on his intelligence, in the light of his examination marks, while I study and construct his character for myself. I then write a dozen lines of general conclusions, partly technical, and partly based on my own impressions.

If one night these poor people were to smash up the office archives, they might well come in their hundreds to ask me what right I had to describe them as I have—patient or impatient, calm, highly strung, touchy, brutal—when I know them so little. A frightening thought. The archives should be locked up like a strong-room. What really counts above all in these examinations is intuition, true intuition; but to the person judged, it must always seem offensive, an arbitrary sentence pronounced by a stranger.

The type of applicant with which I am faced is unknown to me, since I have never worked down here before. Nevertheless, the technique, the methods have always to be the same. The interviewer sits glued to his chair for hours, while the candidates come and go; so many pass before his table that he hardly sees them as they walk into the room, sit down or get up to go. He takes them in only when they are seated and speaking: then he scrutinizes them as they appear to him, like a head-and-shoulders photograph, and tries to lead them on into revealing something about their lives. How long have you been unemployed? Have you children? A wife? A mother? Do you read the papers? Whereabouts do you live? Have you travelled at all?

If one has to allocate particular men to particular work, and there is a normal—one might say natural—disparity between the number of applicants and places available (but in the employer's favour), psychotechnical methods offer a reliable means of selection and of discovering individual aptitudes: this much has been proved. But here the factory is not choosing a group of workers to be divided up according to their abilities and our requirements. Here we are judging a whole people. The chosen few may be taken on by us, but what is to happen to those who are rejected? One reads in the press that unemployment is a cancerous growth, the gravest threat to our society; but one must see it and feel its effects in order fully to realize this. It makes all recourse to the use of reason—of which psychotechnology is a recent development—seem simply pointless. It is a sieve. One does not select, one skims. This morning, in the silence of my office during the written tests, two phrases kept repeating themselves in my mind: that it would be easier for a camel to pass through the eye of a needle than for an inhabitant of Santa Maria to get through this psychological examination; and that we were, so to speak, confronting them with a funnel, into which a river enters at one end and only a trickle comes out at the other.

Saturday

In an attempt to make the candidates understand the situation by the use of symbols, I have begun to use the phrases that came into my mind during the examinations. The interviews naturally become transformed into a desperate appeal on their side. I had started the day with a workman in his forties, who had done fairly well in the tests, to which he had been admitted out of pity, or weakness, or in order to rid ourselves of his perpetual presence; certainly not in the likelihood of his being useful to us, given his age. As a personnel officer I have to make every possible effort, in the face of desperation such as his, to get the situation and our point of view accepted as reasonable.

I tried the simile of the funnel, as being the more logical and least brutal: the other—the eye of the needle—has a too biblical sound. A third—that of the women who in buying their tomatoes choose only the best—would not do either. In any case, it is already clear that no appeal to reason is worth while and that the narrowness of the funnel is at least not "directly" our fault. To escape blame altogether we should not have set up a factory down here at all. The truth is that there will be many good workers who will not be selected; indeed, we can take only the very best from among them: and none now, at once. The factory accepts the best, but they will only be gradually absorbed as production slowly expands. We are continuing our examinations, to keep alive in our breasts, and theirs, the hope that the factory will soon double, treble its size; and to create a reserve of labour, while we fill our immediate requirements with the *crème de la crème*. Many people, judging us in cold blood, from a distance, may disapprove of this method; but it is the only thing to do . . .

Sunday

One gets used to it. During these days the Signorina has been observing me without remarking that I should get used to it, but I have read her thoughts. One must become inured to such a situation if one has to decide the fate of so many people every day. Probably she herself is remorseful at having done so, and the indignation of her new colleague—an indignation betrayed only by a sigh, or some gesture of despair—recalls to her mind her own feelings at the time of her first arrival here. She has never shown a sign of cynicism at my attitude, for naturally she is no less humane in her feelings than I am. She has just wisely awaited the passage of time, in the fatalistic way of the south.

They all give similar answers to the questions which, while maintaining the same end in view, one does one's best to vary. It is almost always the way with workmen; nevertheless, they make themselves understood. And one learns to pick up with all of them the thread that keeps them tied to the place—Santa Maria, Castello, Grotte or to the city itself—where they have always lived. The interviewer comes to know the disposition of the people before familiarizing himself with the district that they come from, where he has never set foot or which he has merely passed through: for in these first weeks I have gone up and down the coastal road as though it were a corridor, seeing nothing of the surrounding country. I have just glimpsed Santa Maria from above, stretched along the sea and clustering round its old castle; a lovely sight.

On this Sunday evening, with the factory silent and empty—only the gate-keeper at the entrance and an assistant assigned to us at the laboratory—nothing remained in my mind but the passing before me of those sad dark eyes, the whole week through. Nothing else, and no one in particular. Only the last of all.

Even the most intelligent or highly skilled were ready to accept any kind of work. It would have been ingenuous in the extreme to enquire what sort of job they preferred. They all proclaimed themselves ready even to clean out the lavatories, as though the factory were one great latrine. At the most, they might indicate a preference for mechanical work. I said to the last one this evening, a sensible and talkative lad who wanted to be a mechanic: "But you see, ours is an odd sort of mechanical work. It is mass-produced. You wouldn't be doing the kind of mechanical work that you have in mind . . . You might find it monotonous, boring . . ." He did not react at all, but remained seated in a state of suspense in which his reasoning powers seemed completely paralysed; or else he was afraid there might be some catch in what I said.

And so I found myself alone again, in the starry twilight, with no more candidates.

CHAPTER II

Monday

ACROSS THE WIDE entrance-hall of the factory, cooled by the morning air, silent and sweet-smelling (some special oil is used for the red paving-tiles) goes the Lombard general staff—tall and fair, a different race from the locals. Leaving behind them the quiet of the drawing-office they stride purposefully towards the workshops and the insistent clamour of the machines. One instinctively falls back, respectfully, before them.

At present, however, it is with the Lombards that I like talking; the character of each is so easy to read, and we are able to compare our experiences in the factories from which we have been transferred, with their common memories, traditions and famous names.

The southerners, those that come from Santa Maria, are all more alike in their attitude, having a similar pride in their jobs; knowing no better, they believe that this is the only establishment of its kind, a blessed isle in an empty sea, although this district is becoming an industrial one.

When one sees the Lombards approaching together, they have an overbearing air about them. But I have already made friends with one of these fair-haired men, the most unassuming in manner, who is head of the tool-room. Here one can talk, for the noise is not deafening, and the men move quietly and with ease about the benches and machinery. In this department are the machines that make the tools and stamps for the "mass-production" machines (those that turn out our products, in their thousands) and the work is slow, precise, consisting of single parts or small batches. Here, one man can still carry through a long job on the same piece of stubborn steel, intent on the quality of his work rather than on the time-factor.

The machinery has been painted blue and the parts in movement bright orange, to guard against accidents. On the polished floor the workers are dispersed among the machines, and it almost seems as though no one is there.

From the windows facing west, towards the island, the slanting rays of the setting sun caught the faces of the men in their blue overalls, as I entered, with a rose-coloured reflection. They work in a liquid, idyllic glow.

To me, and to others, industry has seemed till now to consist of a dense crowd of men and machines beneath the north-lit, saw-toothed roofs of the great workshops. It seems strange to me to bring the brightness of sun, sky and sea, and the greenery of lawns and trees, right into a factory, much as I love them. I myself was born in central Italy and spent my boyhood in a city of the south, so that I have become a southerner. But my experience of industry has been in the north, where, if it is true industry, it is always dark in hue. Workshops to me are dim and crowded, as though their very strength lay in these characteristics.

Ripamonti, the head of the tool-room, can understand this, for he comes from the north. He is an innately responsible, educated and dignified man; but he has a ready smile, with his rather full lips in a sensitive face. We had begun by remarking on the novelty of the painted machines, of which he was rather proud, though somewhat sceptical; for however meticulous he may be in the field of technique and output, he holds it his duty to exercise full criticism where his department is concerned. He stops, if anywhere, at new theories. I felt some reluctance at broaching the inevitable subject that dominates everything here, however awkward, indeed displeasing, one may feel it to be. Would the southern workers justify the hopes placed in them?

"How are the workers doing?" I asked quietly.

He smiled with satisfaction, as he glanced at his men.

"They're doing very well now, I'm extremely pleased with them."

"But at first?"

"At first they were always trying to show off; boasting about their work, if you see what I mean, Doctor, instead of showing what they could do. I had to explain that I wanted deeds, not words: Bring me the part, I would say; I don't want all this talk, it means nothing to me. Bring me the part you have made . . . Now we get on splendidly." He smiled again, in his guarded way. "I hold them now in the hollow of my hand," he concluded quietly.

At the centre of the workshops—the centre of the cross, for they are comprised in four arms that radiate out into the garden at the foot of the bare hillside—in the very midst of the hubbub of the machines, the clear light from the sky floods in at the windows, and all about one is the fresh green of near-by trees. The site is so spacious that the layout of the building has been designed on the freest of lines, and the visitor, finding himself surrounded by machinery, but, as it were, on the edge of a wood or a meadow, is rather taken aback.

All the same, the repetitive and monotonous work of mass-production, of the machines that make the many thousands of parts for our products, penetrates everywhere, and fills our ears and brains with its clatter.

The men at the automatic lathes stand watchfully at their posts, or move round their machines which, spurting out oil, have to be fed by them with long bars of steel. They keep a check on the tools of the turret-head; while below, thousands of small parts fall into the bins, like so much grain. The workers at the drills and presses have jobs that are more monotonous and strictly timed. They turn out hundreds of thousands of parts an hour, with a speed that seems unnecessarily forced, but which is required for regularity of output. All young men, they imperceptibly exert an always increasing pressure in order not to be overcome with inertia. In this lies their labour: it is not evident, because their regularity of movement, demanded by the piece-work system, seems easy and continuous.

It is difficult and deadening work. One immediately recognizes the protagonist of mass-production, the worker who is halfway between craftsmanship and automation: a manual worker, but a specialized one, doing repetitive but skilled work. He is interchangeable like the parts he produces, but he is possessed of the carefulness and responsibility of a technician.

It is this contradiction that worries us industrial psychologists, although it fascinates us: for it tends to break up the human personality while at the same time it places great responsibility upon the worker.

Amidst all this noisy machinery it is difficult to speak to anyone. Moreover, the skilled worker is, as a rule, not talkative. But at the end of the southern arm of the building, where various kinds of heat treatment are carried out, there is silence; and the atmosphere is humid, with acid fumes.

A charge-hand from Santa Maria, sturdily built, with lightish hair and blue eyes, took me to a corner where one could breathe more easily. His overall was open at the neck and he was sweating, giving out the same odour of fatigue that we had had in the examination room.

He was a true worker, older than the others. After having explained to me, in his own words, how the piece-work system functioned, he compared it with that of other factories: since ours is a new one, some of the workers on piece-rates earn more than those charge-hands who, like himself, are not yet fully qualified, in other words, still trainees, and who draw a fixed wage. This discouraged him. Having let it out, as though unintentionally and objectively, he screwed up his eyes, respectful, but perplexed, and remained standing beside me. His voice was hoarse.

"Where were you before?"

"I was at the steel-works for five years, as a pattern-maker."

"Joinery?"

"Yes, Doctor. This factory is much finer, one is better off here. And then the basic wage is higher . . . that's why I came." His eyes narrowed again. "What can one do, we are all so badly off in these parts." He added, apologetically, "But for me this cellulosing job has not been . . . progress. I found more satisfaction in my work before. I have had to give up my craft." He remained silent, still standing over me, and I pretended to find his confession natural. But this was not so, because we are already too much accustomed to praise.

Tuesday

"Oh, no one ever comes here, Doctor. You're much better off in the administration wing," grinned the foreman of the cellulosing section; and at once made ready to conduct me—his colleague, guest, superior: he seemed uncertain which—round his department.

We watched the little frames of the calculators, like tiny motor-cars, sliding along the conveyor on their complicated course, during which they are cellulosed, coated with enamel, dried, re-cellulosed and finally dried again by the heat of very powerful lamps.

We passed the ovens; we went round the inferior work of a non-mechanical kind; and paused at the electrolytic vessels into which the parts are plunged for plating with nickel or chromium. My guide bestowed on them a slight grimace of contempt, although he was careful to explain them to me, being proud of the chemical complexity of the processes.

For a while we stopped behind the men who were preparing small parts for immersion in the vats. Each part had to be slipped on to the wire dipping-frames, and the men, seated before them, worked at a great rate, hooking one after another on to one row after another, from left to right and from the top downwards, as though filling a page with writing. The foreman glanced at me. He was aware that these workers do not find their job interesting, but this does not worry him overmuch; whereas we, of the personnel office, are accustomed to regard it as one well suited for psycho-social study and research.

When one frame is finished, it is lifted off, packed and jingling with parts, and another begun. Nowadays, the frames are moved vertically by a pedal, in other words they can be raised and lowered in such a way as to keep the line that has to be filled at arm-level; formerly the workers had to bend down for the lower lines; a back-breaking job. The movable frame has been a technical and social conquest.

Each worker, like a child with his abacus, was threading each piece by means of a little hole in the hook, in one movement of the arm; then another piece; then another. When one row was finished, the process was repeated.

Among them was an elderly man who had been taken on because he was disabled. He heard us behind him, but did not turn round. He lifted his arms slowly to find the hooks, one by one, while the others could now do it without looking. He stumbled on, with the meticulous care of the old, his thin back bent over his work.

"The others are getting on well," said the foreman. "Not this one. You'll have to remove him."

But who would have him?

"It's work for women, really. If it weren't that we have always to give priority to the men, because of the unemployment here . . ." I paused.

His eyes narrowed, and he said stiffly: "Anyway, our women in the south wouldn't come and work here. We aren't in Northern Italy, Doctor . . ." There was silence.

Near by, other workers, the most shabbily clad in the factory and wearing clogs, were putting the frames into vats of steaming acid. They all lifted their caps to us, pleased at the notice taken of them. But the foreman wanted to hurry me away, unwilling to let me stop— out of all his department—precisely with those who were dressed in rags.

He was anxious to show me the work at the benches, of which he was particularly proud: three men hammering the chassis to straighten them out, and filing the join between frame and cover in order that it should fit well. Although they work at the mass-production machines their job is an individual one. They have to trust their intuition, their eyes, their artistry, as in wrought iron-work; and the final result varies in quality and in the time it takes. There is nothing that a worker enjoys more.

He had wanted to present this group to me, but they slipped away, having no time to spare. All the workers at the benches are independent, and rather conceited.

Then he took the cover of a chassis to adjust himself, caressing it with his finger-tips to feel the surface; and, grasping a hammer, gave it two or three blows to flatten out an edge. He squinted along it. No, even I could see, it wasn't straight. With a crestfallen look, he gave it another blow, and improved it.

"I'm out of practice," he said. "They're better at it now than I am. Since I became foreman, I've lost my skill. But it was I who trained the team." He constantly regretted the trade of the true mechanic.

"Over there is the spray-booth," he said, pointing at the glass cabin with an ambiguous smile. With leather apron, gum-boots and gloves the celluloser sprays the chassis of the calculators with a kind of pistol, his face masked by a respirator. Working in clouds of cellulose, he was hardly aware of our presence.

As soon as we had left the cabin, the foreman asked me why we were not issuing milk to the cellulosers. "We have been asking for it now for a month, but there's been no sign of it yet." As it happens, the doctors no longer consider that milk is useful against chemical poisoning; they think it even harmful. But the impression had been given that we grudged the milk.

"I'll report it to the management."

We made our way to the exit of the department in silence. The foreman, at my side, looked closely at me; he was respectful, but still rather perplexed, and he repeated: "Every day they expect that milk."

CHAPTER III

Wednesday

ONLY THREE CANDIDATES have got through our last set of examinations; and no one has been taken on.

The second of them, dressed in a dark blue suit with white stripes, his thick hair smalmed down with brilliantine, had a job in a life insurance office. Not that this mattered, because here we turn fishermen, barmen, bathing attendants and guards from the numerous prisons of the district into members of the working-class; but this chap was too glib altogether, and tried to get the better of the interviewer. Perhaps he took me for a possible client.

Before him I had interviewed an ingenuous young man from Santa Maria; and I had asked him what films he had seen lately. "*Bathing Belles*, with Esther Williams."

It seemed that they had been talking to one another in the waiting-room. The insurance clerk was now sitting, smart and self-possessed, with me. For him, it was child's-play, chatting and answering questions; fiddling with a ring on his finger, he was ready to talk of this and that, as one man of the world to another. In the course of this brilliant conversation came my question: "And have you seen any good films lately?"

"Oh, a marvellous one, Doctor. *Bathing Belles*, with Esther Williams."

"Ah, did you like the principal actress? Do you remember her name?"

"No, Doctor, frankly, I do not remember it. You know, I go to the cinema, sometimes alone, sometimes with friends, but I pay more attention to the story than the actors; all this business of stars, baby stars, famous stars, Doctor . . . Nowadays people go to the cinema just to see the actress . . ."

"That's true. But the leading lady is Esther Williams."

"Yes, of course, Doctor. Esther Williams, beautiful, shapely . . ."

"And then, how well she dresses!"

"Ah, extremely elegant, a real lady. That sort of elegance, though, if I may say so, very rich and showy"—he pursed his lips—"you see, we Italians . . ."

"You don't care for that kind of elegance?" He turned his mobile face towards me with a questioning air, his eyebrows cocked. "Those showy evening-dresses, those American fashions, Doctor . . . We Italians have simpler tastes, any little frock is good enough for us; we prefer what's inside it."

"Oh, so you didn't see enough of that? She was too often in evening-dress?"

"Oh, yes, Doctor, always long evening-dresses, jewels, furs."

"But . . ."

"You understand me, Doctor."

"But, after all, she was usually bathing."

Although the actress had been useful psychologically, that was enough of Esther Williams: I closed the interview. I bade him good-bye, and went across to look at the sea, already veiled by the mid-day haze.

The third was Michele Pizza, in the full strength of his thirty years; being one, according to his report, of a numerous family of brothers and sisters, among them a midwife. His round, eager eyes beneath his strongly modelled forehead were turned at once on me to ask: "Is there any hope for me, Doctor?"

There was nothing for it, as we sat together, but to try to check, to fend off, as it were, his passion for work; and I was tempted—instead of questioning him—to talk too much, to explain and excuse myself. Technically, this is a mistake; it is the easiest bad habit that an inter-viewer can fall into when, finding himself at a loss for some reason or feeling that his intuition is failing him, he fills the void with speech; only to end up full of himself without having understood anything of the mystery before him. If I smiled and hinted that there might be hope for him, this young man leant forward like a child who tries too soon to grasp a toy from the hands of a grown-up; but no sooner did I indicate the difficulties than he sank back dejectedly as though I were snatching it away. Driven to it, I had to conclude by saying that no applicant had more than one chance in a hundred of being taken on, perhaps one in a thousand.

His eyes filled with tears; a deep, tragic sigh broke from him, a murmur: I have been unemployed for five years, Doctor, I have been looking for a job for five years. He had been seeking it with frenzy, and he had reached the pitch of his frenzy before my table.

I steadied the conversation with a few questions, to distract his mind. A man's tears are unbearable; they cannot be either noticed or for-bidden. He seemed almost absent-minded. Questions about himself and his life appeared odd to him, and made him suspicious.

He lives near my own house, and smiled with gentle astonishment as I told him of my difficulties in finding one near Castello. "But, Doctor," he said brightly, "there are so many houses, big houses here. Why didn't you ask me?"

"I didn't know you! Is it something that you do?"

"Oh, yes, I could have managed something. I help a friend who has an agency."

"How do you spend your time?"

The question embarrassed him at once; he shook his head and struggled against the temptation not to reply.

"What do you expect . . . when one's been unemployed for five years? . . . One does one thing and another . . ."

"But couldn't you tell me, simply, as you would a friend, how you spend your day?" He understood that he was to reveal something intimate, that sincerity would help him, but that the psychologist was anxious, too, not to force his privacy.

"I get up late . . . In the morning I help my mother and sisters about the house . . . I have a meal. In the afternoon I go out with friends, have a walk, go to the café . . . I go to some club or a cinema, but seldom, Doctor, I haven't the . . ." He stuck at the word. "And then I pick up some job or other. The agency . . . through it I'm sometimes asked to do some house-repairs. Or I help my other sister, the midwife."

I did not ask how he helped the midwife.

"Do you go about looking for these jobs, or do people send to you?"

"No, no," he replied, his eyes untroubled now and his agonized desire for work momentarily appeased. "I wait to be sent for."

He was a good fellow, and likeable; I felt drawn to him, although he bore the stamp of unemployment like a mask upon his face, as of an ineluctable fate. As a matter of fact he had bungled most of the tests for no apparent reason: unless it were a matter of some unconscious defence of his own state, of a deeply rooted disbelief in the possibility of change.

The three of them, and their reports, went up for their brief interviews with the Manager. They were soon back, a *no* against all of them. For that matter, my own summing-up of each one had been very doubtful; they had all done badly in the exams. We have to choose better material altogether. Every man has his good qualities alongside his defects, and it is easy to let oneself be seduced by the former. This is another mistake into which one is prone to fall, in the work of selecting: the mistake of being almost more struck by a gleam in the darkness than by total clarity. For instance, certain remarks made by stupid candidates, or their signs of intuitive understanding, may fascinate a psychologist almost as much as if they issued from a well of brilliance.

Having been hastily paid their expenses and told they would be written to, the simple-minded lad from Santa Maria, the insurance clerk with his talk of Esther Williams, and the midwife's brother all went away bewildered, after a morning they would certainly not forget in a hurry.

There is a continual conflict between the intense ardour for work that animates the applicants here and the suspicion they arouse of being, involuntarily, habituated to intrigue, to string-pulling and to idleness. On the one hand they are spurred on by a blind, restless desire for work combined with a fixed, inveterate habit of seeking work rather than working; and on the other, they are inured to a state of unemployment, which is so deeply rooted that it has generated its own vices and its own natural defences.

These vices and defences are exasperating, if one forgets that they are historical in origin. The lamentations, the offers of service, the persistence of some candidates are irritating in the extreme. One begins to see deception all about one, a country where lies flourish, a country that can only be given up as hopeless. Then one reads again the immemorial sadness and fear in their eyes, as they stand before one—their self-respect at odds with their obsequiousness and their hope—and I feel myself a southerner once more.

The interviews and intelligence tests raise a protective barrier between us and them, between the factory and the town: they are our defence, too, against unemployment. Unemployment makes psychological methods, which should be neutral, immoral, because they become influenced by the place where they are operating. Scientific selection and unemployment exclude one another. If the demand and supply of labour are balanced, scientific selection can be a help to the workers themselves, directing them towards work that suits them, a guide as to their abilities, rather than an absolute assessment of their merits. (A sociologist has observed that it is no good deciding in the laboratory that a group of workers may be suited to work in a bottle factory, if the bottle factories of the district are all closing.)

Selection on psychological lines is not a final judgment: a man can always improve, or at least change. But with us, the sieve has to be too fine, not owing to ill-will on our part or because our technique is too strictly applied: but simply in proportion to the excess of applicants over vacancies.

Fortunately, one becomes better at this work of selection all the time, whether owing to intuition or experience it is hard to say. The fear of treating human beings merely as objects, as goods, forces one to be honest. Remorse at judging one's fellow-men is alleviated by one's faith in an ability always to make fewer mistakes; and by the consciousness that selection is a necessity. One selects, because one has work to offer.

The more fortunate they are in penetrating through the narrow door from which most are sent away, the more they find themselves subjected to pronounced changes of atmosphere. In the course of a few hours they pass from the cold douche of the examinations to the warm one of the interview, and then again to the brief cold plunge of the appointment with the Manager, who can only see them for a moment to sum up—mysteriously it seems to them—their qualifications. It is a good method for tempering raw material. They find themselves, in the interview, led into a friendly conversation: for otherwise they would be obstinately mute, and it would only be possible to note a timid or aggressive disposition, without understanding them at all. But in the interview they forget that they are being summed up, and think that this informal talk is a sign that they are to be engaged; indeed, that we particularly want them and cannot do without them.

For that matter, the interview is always a difficult and unsatisfactory method, because it depends on the medium to which the worker is least accustomed, the spoken word: whereas manual work lies at the opposite pole to the capacity for expression. It is bad for them if they do not speak, and bad, too, if they talk too much, or at random.

And least of all, in the interview, can a candidate's consistent moral development be foreseen, or the solution that time will effect: the man who is looking forward with his whole being escapes immediate diagnosis, and the sum total of his marks today may not represent him as he will be tomorrow. This is the fortune-teller's risk: I shall not know whether I have been right or wrong until months have passed, and then only as regards those who have been taken on. The rejected will not come up for judgment any more.

One feels one ought to live for a long time with a candidate before guaranteeing to know him, and to reply conscientiously to the question as to whether we should engage him. Instead, we have to do the exact opposite: our methods are those of a condensed form of knowledge of the man, made necessary by haste and by the crowd of applicants.

Moreover, we cannot be helped by any form of self-criticism or self-judgment on the part of the candidates themselves. They are not going to tell us what form of work they prefer, or are likely to be good at. If we told them to stand on their heads for eight hours on end in the factory, they would accept. But afterwards? It would seem that their first step will be to attain the consciousness of being workers—not even a class-consciousness—and that these fortunate ones will find more cause to complain than the rest. Yet how in the world are they living today? Where do they get that bare minimum of sustenance? And once they are engaged by us, what will be the state of mind of these un-employed, used as they are to dividing their time between their families and the streets: what, confined in a factory, will be their out-put, their productivity—indeed, their happiness—along the years?

The possibility that—apart from being engaged—they might be able to choose one kind of work rather than another, leaves them unmoved, since they fear that, in stating some preference, they may limit their chances. So they all continue to offer to clean out the lavatories.

According to the experts, the trouble lies not with unemployment but with lack of training. The writers of articles on the subject in the economic journals are sarcastic at the expense of ingenuous sympath-izers or demagogues who rail against an impossible situation. There is a superabundance of labourers and manual workers, certainly. But try and find a trained man, with qualifications, in the south! You will fail.

Yet why should one abolish lack of training before abolishing un-employment? Better do away with both together.

It may well be asked, too, why—in waiting for automation, for which nothing but engineers will be needed—we should exaggerate the qualities required by mass-production? Many tasks are still of a kind to be done by manual workers, although they are specialized.

There is always the same reasonable answer: that when one can choose, it is only human, on the part of those who direct production and whose duty it is to produce the best and the most that is possible in a given time, always to prefer a trained to an untrained man, even for ordinary work. Unless the disparity between a man's abilities and the grade of work is so great that it will affect his output, it is natural always, everywhere, to seize on the best that is offered. Even in moving packing-cases, intelligence comes in. A foreman requiring a manual worker will say that he does not want to be given a half-wit, because the half-wit will shift the cases clumsily and let them fall.

Thursday

The factory is everything to us, down here. Even the near-by city does not interest us. I live halfway between the two, but even at night, if I go out, it seems natural to make my way towards the factory, standing on its hillside like a fantastic, illuminated castle.

It seems an end in itself, rather than a means. Nevertheless, the world does not end in the factory, which is surrounded by more than just a landscape.

The other face, the deceptive face of the factory, is that it induces in us employees and managing staff a kind of colonialism; and, in the men who are taken on, the pride of a workers' aristocracy, which—more even than in the north—cuts their bonds with their own class: a dangerous sort of pride, not political or national, but industrial. We have to get away from the factory in order to feel ourselves what, indeed, we are—a drop in the ocean. Outside it, in the country, or along the coast, we merge with the rest of our fellows. Beyond it there is a collective life to which the factory brings only a mirage of civilization.

The illiterates do not know that their humiliation is ours too. With all our science and our organization, we cannot help them when they brandish a pencil. The privileged status of the firm comes up against them and against the distant State, of which we are the accomplices.

As for me, I should like to live altogether in the country that I have to traverse four times a day. Instead, although my house is there, I am drawn to the factory and back as though through a transparent tunnel, cut off from the open air, the fresh sea-breezes and the sun.

Friday

It rained this afternoon. An unusual grey mist blended sky and sea in one, and made the factory buildings look drab and massive, despite their coloured walls and light roofs. They almost took on an appropriately industrial air.

But when one arrives in the morning, on a fine day, what a delight it is to see the airy, graceful lines of the covered way with its slender columns, against the sea. Our work is gladdened by the beauty of the factory among its flowers and pine-trees, and by the marvel of the warm, scented air.

CHAPTER IV

Monday

MY FIRST MORNING at the assembly lines.

I came in to find that the supervisor, the Lombard time-keeper, was not there. There was an unusual buzz of talk—with the cat away, the mice were at play—and the older men were in charge of the more difficult stages of the assembling and the final testing. Someone had left his place and was shouting to another three benches away. One worker, an adept at imitating the crowing of a cock with the pneumatic drill, was filling the place with cock-a-doodle-do's. We all laughed at him, until the supervisor appeared at the end of the room.

I approached a youth who was doing a fairly simple job, because I was to try the same sort of thing myself. His hands were jerking backwards and forwards; he did not move the tool from the bench by pushing it, but by making it jump away with a sharp knock. He did this with an even movement, and an air of detachment; continuing serenely as I watched him, he waited for me to speak.

He had been born at Santa Maria and had lived in Liguria. His mother came from the north. He had been down here, and working in the factory, for a year and a half. It bored him. With a self-confident air he said: "I'm waiting for them to replace me by a woman. This job is too easy. In northern Italy a woman would do it." In fact, it seemed easy enough; but we are not taking on any more women because we are overwhelmed with applications from unemployed men. I only gave him a hint of this in order not to dash his hopes and because even those who have been engaged by us have their doubts about our problems; when we talk of our forty thousand applications even the most open-minded of the locals, those who are neighbours of the unemployed, show compunction, but are unconvinced. This boy, anyway, complains too much of boredom, although he is near to earning full piece-work rates.

Having watched what he was doing for a time, I sat down at an empty place behind him. I had to take a small steel container, like a rectangular box with perforated and indented edges, and fit it into a mechanism on the bench. Ten metal rods carrying at their ends ten numbers from 0 to 9 then had to be aligned, in order, into the indentations. Small springs had to be fitted between the rods.

Only by correct handling would the mechanism depress the springs all together and fit them into their places. When this had been done, one had to remove the container and, while endeavouring not to let the springs jump out, slip on an indented plate as a kind of lid. Then the lid had to be fixed on the box by two screws, leaving the springs and the metal rods imprisoned, with the numbers sticking out. To do all this, seventy-three seconds were allowed.

Before me on the bench was a case with two shelves and ten compartments, four above and six below. Those above contained the noughts, twos, threes and ones, and those below the fours, sixes, eights, nines, sevens and fives. This is reasonable; if one extended one's two hands from the sides towards the middle of the case, first above and then below, one could take the numbers in order without looking. On my left I had a heap of the little boxes, to my right the indented plates. I had a measure for controlling the gap between the pieces when mounted; a box of screws; a screwdriver; a pair of pincers; and against my stomach, but attached to the bench, the box of springs, like small worms.

I began with one hand only; with two, I should have taken longer. I put my mind on to the work, because I had to learn the sequence of movements. I did not even look at the clock. I slipped the numbers on and gently put the springs in place. When they were all aligned, I applied pressure by means of the mechanism. Some of the springs fitted into their places, but not all. To adjust the recalcitrant ones I opened the mechanism for a moment with my fingers: the whole lot immediately jumped out and scattered themselves all over the place. They bounced on the floor, or found their way into my new, starched overall; but I set to at once, with new ones, or with such of the old as I could recover.

Some springs always stick, and others jump about like fleas. I was ashamed of the way I wasted them. But I finally got them all into alignment. Then I had to put on the indented plate. If one does not do this correctly, the springs rise up again, and it is useless to attempt to control them by pressure alone. They take their revenge by coming out crooked, so that the plate does not fit and cannot be screwed down. There, this time I had done it properly. But even securing the screws is difficult, although it looks simple enough.

At last I had completed the adjustment of the first part.

The first parts are all equally difficult; it is the correct handling of the mechanism that baffles one. I was so worried by the work that the machine-shop seemed to disappear from around me. I had to begin

B

each part over and over again, two or three times, and naturally I could only take the numbers out with one hand. This was where the skill, the manual dexterity that we look for in the tests was wanted, together with the subtle, slender fingers.

Having mounted some parts with difficulty I discovered a way of controlling these agile springs. I cannot say how; but it was the first imperceptible sign of my training. In other words, I had learnt to manœuvre the mechanism at least mentally. I might not succeed, but I knew in my own mind what I had to do.

A glance at my wrist-watch warned me that when seventy-three seconds had passed I was still halfway through the process. At my rate of work the factory would soon close down, after being forced to increase its production of springs . . .

A passing charge-hand smiled at my efforts; his attitude was one of friendly, ironical good-humour, which would be not so usual in the case of a real learner. At the bench in front of me the young southern-born Ligurian continued steadily, hardly even moving his head. To my left I discovered another man I knew, doing the same work as I was: he had been examined by me, and smiled gravely at me, nervous at my presence. But when I was working, I was unconscious of everything around me, seeing and hearing nothing.

The charge-hand had gone down the staircase leading to the work-shops. The supervisor, too, must have gone away again, because at the other end of the room, where the calculating machines are half-mounted, the cock-a-doodle-do of the automatic drill was again to be heard, accompanied by talk and laughter. Animated by the general good-humour, the cock crowed several times, now briefly, now with a long-drawn-out squawk; then changed into short whistles like a siren. The laughter merged with the noise of the machinery and enlivened the whole atmosphere. A few broke off work, in spite of the timing. Even we of the easy stages were laughing, and I caught the eye of my neighbour, inviting him to relax his gravity. Suddenly the supervisor eturned.

I seized an indented plate, resolved to mount it perfectly and more quickly, without making a single mistake. One had to keep one's mind on it the whole time, while letting the hands work automatically; but it is precisely this effort of the will that ties one's movements. The good intention of taking the numbers with both hands, of juggling with the mechanism and of controlling the vices, holds one up. Luckily I noticed that I had collected some dozen parts already finished, which were to be put into the machines that were for sale. It takes a good many weeks to achieve the correct rhythm of forty pieces an hour: but I shall not have to undergo this test.

My back was aching. Once more I saw nothing but the level floor of the bench and was oblivious of the noise around me. Finally, the sound of the bell relieved me from the assembly lines.

Tuesday

I am making progress in the technique of this work, because I carry forward a little experience from the mounting of one piece to another. But I cannot yet relax and trust myself to work automatically, which is the secret of training for mass-production. I think about it: I think rightly, but my instinct is wrong. All the same, I find manual work exciting for the time being.

I wanted to speak to my neighbour, the worker I had examined myself, and so, my attention wandering for a moment, three springs jumped on to the clean neck of the Ligurian in front of me. I promptly changed my mind about speaking, because although they do not expect anything from me in the way of output, I am not supposed to provide examples of the way in which accidents occur. I glanced again at the novice beside me: he had curly hair, a small head like a bird and a long nose. He was much quicker at the work than I was, yet he seemed to move heavily, unlike the dexterous Ligurian. He did not take the numbers with both hands, nor did he even insert them all at once, but gathered them together and pushed them; finally he slowly screwed the lid down with the screwdriver. After a week he was completing 225 pieces a day, and was therefore a hundred short on his eight hours.

He was not doing badly, however, considering that he was a secondary schoolboy. We are always rather afraid of engaging these halfway clerical workers.

At the age of twenty he had got into trouble with a girl and had had to marry. He is resigned and contented, even though he can no longer hope to be a civil servant. When we summoned him for the medical examination (a sign that, if fit, he would be taken on) his face lit up with joy, although he is an extremely shy lad.

He is getting on well, in his silent way, and is exhibiting a perseverance similar to my own; that of one determined to demonstrate that in spite of everything he can do skilled manual work. Clumsy, but zealous for his own *amour-propre*, with a consciousness both of his downfall and his good fortune in having achieved security, he is becoming an excellent worker; one of the gentle, shy sort, solitary even during the lunch-break.

Wednesday

I am anxious about my neighbour's results, for we have got to put up a good show, both of us. I took the responsibility of accepting his standard of schooling, and, in an establishment like ours, selector and selected feel a bond between them, almost as that between a godfather and his godchildren. From the trouble he takes over his work and the attention he pays me without letting his attention wander, I should say that he is aware of this.

I had counted the pieces that I had succeeded in finishing, whether well or badly, and found that there were some dozens. I had checked them with the measure. I felt satisfaction; it is a pity that when one repeats a job three hundred times a day one loses this sense of satisfaction in accurate work. My secondary-school accomplice and father of a family watched me out of the corner of his eye.

I went over to look at the preparation of a new assembly line for the later, complicated stages of the work. Here the men took no notice of me; they were the senior workers in the factory, who do not trouble about the personnel officer, being on friendly terms with the engineers and industrial experts. Di Meo, a very highly skilled, bald-headed charge-hand, was teaching a worker who had come on from a simpler stage of the process. He was manipulating an almost completed calculating-machine, and turned it gently about in his hands as a nurse does a baby. "You must work like a blind man, like a blind man," he repeated to the other, scrutinizing the delicate mechanism of the interior. With a very long, needle-like screwdriver the learner was trying to find a small spring far back in the machine's intestines; he turned it. And then? He reversed the machine, though without Dio Meo's gentle skill, and stopped with a perplexed air. A third man approached, and—leaning over the bench and gesticulating—suggested the next operation.

The Lombard supervisor came over from his bench, suspecting trouble. "Don't you see?" he asked, in his strong northern accent. Pointing to the inside of the machine, where one could see nothing at all, he said, "You must get rid of that gap. If you can see light it means there's too much play between the plates." The apprentice did not understand, and asked his teacher for help as the supervisor went back to his bench. Dio Meo took the machine, twiddled it round on the bench and lifted it up to eye-level. "Light getting in," he decided. "Much too big a gap." The learner began to understand; but Di Meo had already grasped the machine and like a juggler had remedied the trouble in the interior. Once this was set to rights, the next operation followed on, automatically. This is the way on the assembly lines: one movement merges into the next. The first is not finished before the second has started, and there are no waits until the whole stage is brought to an end.

The process began again. Di Meo finished the stage. The other worker watched, absorbed, while Di Meo repeated: "You must work like a blind man, like a blind man."

Thursday

At the assembly lines Di Meo was involved in a momentous discussion with a group formed by the supervisor, an engineer from the south, a young charge-hand with a mass of thick hair rising stiffly from his forehead, and four workmen from Di Meo's section. Di Meo was the most excited. I concluded that they were arguing about the time intervals on the new line, because every now and then certain words kept recurring: timing, training, three minutes, three minutes and seven seconds.

In the name of his fellow-workers Di Meo was complaining that the times allotted on this line were too short, that he had tested them himself and could hardly keep to them. He protested, too, to the engineer that the apprenticeship before reaching piece-work lasted too long. It was a half-serious, half-joking discussion, each side being out to gain its point, but in a not unfriendly way, as in disputes in the country between landowners and their peasants. "But you, Di Meo," grinned the engineer, "you must be below your usual form, surely. Anyhow, you're always the one to protest, aren't you?"

"I below my form?" exploded Di Meo, stepping back, horrified, with his hand on his breast. He pretended to be too much astonished to utter a word; and letting his arms fall, turned away, while the engineer discussed the matter seriously with the charge-hand and the supervisor. The other workers shook their heads.

Di Meo returned, gesticulating, to the group, and approaching the engineer said, "Try yourself, sir, try it out yourself . . ." It was then that the charge-hand, always rather solemn and self-important, moved to the centre of the group and imposed silence. He boasted about the speed at which his brother worked when on the assembly lines—he was a champion, the pride of his family—and declared that this brother had found the time allowed for the stage amply sufficient, and had finished it before any of the others.

At this, one of the workers, who a moment before had been on Di Meo's side, could not contain himself. A tall man, with a long face, he was grave as a professor; and he told the charge-hand outright that he himself worked much more quickly than that brother of his. The engineer exclaimed good-naturedly to Di Meo, "You see?" Di Meo, still rebellious, but discouraged, stumped around like a puppet, looking searchingly at his companions, as though still hoping for support. But if there were those who found the stage too slow, as well as those who found it too quick, it must mean that the timing was correct, the required average, as the engineer had tried to show. So what was there to argue about?

"Of course, you're always right," he said ruefully to the engineer. "You engineers are always right." Di Meo was angry, but comical, familiar. The engineer laughed and made a show of fending him off.

An industrial dispute in miniature was thus happily resolved, as it were, in the family.

Returning towards my office I stopped to look at one of the newly completed adding machines which, without its chassis, was being run in electrically for two hours. It is this running in that fills the workshop with its eternal noisy humming. A lean, lively workman approached, and when I had watched it for some time, he turned to me and said in my ear: "You see, Doctor. I control all these machines myself. I remove the motors and reattach them. If I don't remove them in time, they burn out. I'm here all day, running to and fro, I have to have a hundred eyes, I have to guard the machines. There used to be another here, but now I do it all. I can't leave for a moment, I haven't time even to go to the toilet." He waited for me to show how impressed I was. Again he murmured: "It's a great responsibility, Doctor." "Yes, you have great responsibility," I said, although it was only one of the usual jobs for a specialized manual worker. With a knowing smile that illumined his pale, hollow cheeks and with a gleam in his eyes, he said, still more confidentially: "Excuse me, Doctor. You are the phizzycologist, aren't you? They say that you only have to see a man to tell whether he is intelligent or half-witted."

He seemed pleased in a sly way. After so much walking round the factory I was at last hearing the voice of the people.

"But no one is half-witted here," I exclaimed, startled. He was delighted, proud to have got the ear of the personnel officer himself, the doctor from the mysterious laboratory, the key of which was kept by the guards like that of the strong-room. He grinned at me: "Ah, Doctor, you only have to see a man . . ."

"Don't worry. I am just learning here in the workshops."

"Oh, yes, Doctor, when you see a man . . . You know, the other workers say . . ." But it did not appear to worry him too much. He began again to proclaim his great responsibility. "Doctor, I never move from here. I don't even go to the toilet." Although thin, he seemed well enough; but he did not see that the bushy-haired charge-hand, a few paces away, was signing to me, and tapping his forehead. Passing the machines, with their rattle of keys, I accosted the charge-hand, who drily informed me that the man was a war casualty. "He's one of the disabled ex-soldiers that we have to take. He's a good chap, but queer in the head, Doctor."

CHAPTER V

Friday

AT HALF-PAST FIVE today the factory was invaded by priests. Conducted by a parish priest of the vicinity, they arrived in a black car with a loudspeaker on the roof. No further use, however, was made of their guide, who remained silent during the whole of this mission to the workers. Before the proceedings began, one was aware of a quiet passing to and fro of priestly figures in the drive, between the entrance and the dining-hall, as in the back regions of a sacristy.

The dining-hall is large and well kept; on the side looking towards the open country is a wall entirely of glass, and the tables and chairs are in light wood and steel. During meal-times it is filled with the clamour of voices and the smell of food, particularly of tomato sauce. At other times it remains lifeless and deserted.

Entering the hall at a quarter to six, one saw a number of priests seated in the corners, each at a cleared table; and before every priest a worker in overalls was making his confession. It was hard to tell how this was being done, for not so much as a whisper could be heard, although confessors and penitents alike were not shielded in any way from observation.

A third of the workmen participated in the celebration of Mass, which followed confession.

They stood silently, crowded before the temporary altar, which was set against the wall nearest the kitchens. Above, runs an interior gallery, from which, as soon as the priest had started, the lights of a photographer began to flash. First he took the whole hall, with the workers, then the priest, then some individual groups. He had not been called in by the firm, but belonged to the mission.

We were given a discourse on the moral and religious value of work. But as soon as we were all standing together, with the priest addressing, encouraging, consoling us—this gathering of workers in overalls, this setting for worker-priests—the photographer turned such a blaze of lights upon the whole hall that we were dazzled, blinded, and any piety or emotion that we might have felt was dispelled. I left the hall and went down to the entrance gates, towards the sea. A lorry of the mobile police was stationed outside. The parish priest who had accompanied the mission was standing at the entrance, and since the time of the

service coincided with our closing time he was able to note those of
the workers who left at once, and those who stayed for Mass. One
might have known; this was just the danger.

Later, the young charge-hand with the bushy hair who had attended
Mass and in consequence had lost his bus, was walking along the main
road towards his home, when I stopped my car and picked him up. He
lives beyond the turning to Santa Maria, in one of the colour-washed
cottages that form the factory's modern housing-estate.

After thanking me he sat in silence at my side, with a self-contained
air. Usually, down here, they seize every occasion for a talk. But young
though he looks, with his thick hair and well-cut features, there is a
certain air of arrogance about him. He is undoubtedly one of our
future heads of departments, with his new house and his brother, too,
in the factory. Perhaps he affects taciturnity to distinguish himself from
the other workers, or to show more dignity; or perhaps he really is too
proud.

He sneezed. He had already sneezed three times. Although he had a
heavy cold he would not blow his nose, and made no comment on his
sneezes: this happens rarely among people who work together. I made
no reference to the celebration of Mass, and merely said, "You've
caught a cold. Is there a draught at the assembly lines? Perhaps from
the door on to the office floor?" At our headquarters in the north the
question of draughts in the workshops is one that continually recurs
in the minutes of the works committee.

He shook his head. "No, no I caught a cold yesterday after my
bath, going out on to the terrace, which is near the bathroom." He
added: "Excuse me. It was the sudden change of temperature. Our
bathroom is just beside the terrace."

Since we had reached his destination, he thanked me and got out,
still not blowing his nose; and I made my way up the steep lane to
San Rocco, which I could do with my eyes closed, were it not for the
children, the old people, the carts, and the Americans of the Southern
Nato organization with their cars. Then a piazza opens up, with a bar,
a shop selling mementoes, and the old, gloomy entrance to the
Solfatara crater. Here the poverty of Santa Maria loses itself in the
volcanic land frequented by tourists, with the illusory wealth of its
natural phenomena.

One of the most bewildering rumours that go about the vicinity is
this one concerning the baths. The hot showers in the factory are
confused with the bathrooms in the housing estate. Our workers have
baths every day and go out wrapped in their bath-robes, according to

the peasants round my house, according even to our landlords, and to the men from the cement and steel works who come up from Castello in the evening by the paths that wind among the vines and prickly pears, and whom I was meeting now, in the dark.

Or they go down for the night shift, their bags under their arms. We stop for a chat, as I know some of them. They speak admiringly of the cleanest factory in the world: they who absorb dust through their skins, their mouths and their eyes, and who in their changing-rooms have scarcely a hand-basin.

But cement- and metal-workers are unaware of the problems that cleanliness can arouse. The subject of the factory's hot showers takes first place among the complaints put forward by the members of our works committee.

It would be wrong to blame them, for the trouble arises from a problem of fundamental moral principles, as felt at the most primitive level. Our workers do not raise objections to the temperature or quantity of the water, but to the shifts arranged for women and men, and to the frosted glass doors between the men's showers and the women's. They consider it a danger to morality, after a day's work, to wash themselves in too close proximity to the twenty girls of the testing department, who form the feminine oasis in our factory.

Saturday

A boy was brought in to us at mid-day today. He was wearing a jersey, and his face was scratched and inflamed. Tall as a grown man, although he seemed little more than a child, his long, narrow face was twitching nervously. One of the guards had him by the arm, and dragged him before the Signorina and me.

The guard is of middle-class origin, and has a low, soft voice; he wears his grey uniform with a certain tired, melancholy dignity. He murmured excitedly that the boy, who was a neighbour of his, had spent the night out of doors and had been waiting at the entrance to the factory since daybreak.

"Since daybreak?" asked the Signorina, sharply.

He explained to the Signorina, who was more familiar with the matter than I was, that the boy's uncle had beaten him the previous evening, shouting loud enough for all Santa Maria to hear that he had stolen a piece of bread.

"Tell them yourself," he said to the trembling boy, "tell them what happened."

The boy could not speak. The Signorina said to him forcefully:

"Come, tell us about it, let's hear the latest, so that the doctor, too, can know your story and help you." The boy remained dumb.

"Did you steal the bread?"

At last he was heard to stammer: "No, no, it must have fallen on to the ground. My uncle always blames me because I am not working."

By the look of him, one would have thought he was about fifteen years old. His voice was hoarse, his chest slender and tube-like, his hands long and bony like his face, and even more transparent. The words came in jerks from behind his swollen lips, one of which was cut; but his whole pallid face seemed swollen.

"My uncle ran after me with a knife. I got away, and I'm not going back without work." His voice seemed to come from far away. He was trembling from head to foot.

"But look here, Ugo," said the Signorina, "you must go home now. You are going to have a job here. The Manager has promised you one. Tell your uncle, tell him not to beat you any more. It's no good your staying here." She hurriedly whispered to me: "His uncle is at the M. E. factory, but he hardly ever works. The boy must have been here a dozen times. The Manager has promised him a job, but what can we give him to do? He is twenty years old, but you see what he's like."

To tell the truth, it was hard to imagine him undertaking any work of ours, whether in the tool-shop or at the assembly lines, or even cleaning the famous lavatories: but perhaps this was due to the blow on his mouth and the night spent in the open. The guard whispered again: "There are ten of them, Doctor, orphans. This one's the eldest. I saw it myself, Doctor, his uncle went after him with a knife. He won't go home." Excited by these words, Ugo trembled more than ever.

"We'll inform the Carabineers," declared the Signorina. Ugo appeared indifferent. He waited for us to give him a job.

"Well, Ugo, meanwhile you can go home," said the Signorina, decisively. There was silence. Finally, Ugo murmured obstinately: "I'm not going home without work."

"But where do you want to stay? You can't stop here. If the Manager has promised you work, don't you believe it?"

He nodded, but more bemused than convinced; his face seemed to crumple up, and his hands were shaking. Once more the guard, conscious of his bonds with the people of his birthplace despite his superior status as an educated man who had come down in the world, described Ugo's background. He guaranteed the truth of the situation. Surely we did not doubt his word? The boy was innocent, he was tormented day and night. The Signorina and I looked at one another.

"It's for you to say, Doctor," she said, after another silence. I turned to the boy.

"How is it that your uncle is not in regular work?" I asked, in my usual interview voice.

"Because he has bronchial haemorrhages," replied the boy calmly. "Sometimes in the morning when he gets up to go to work he feels ill and has to sit down. He says that it is I who must work. If I don't he won't let me stay at home. He drives me out of the house."

"Have you looked for a job elsewhere?" He did not reply, seeming not to have taken my question in.

"Where did you sleep last night?"

"I walked about. I didn't steal the bread. But my uncle wants me to bring it home."

"He was round here all night," declared the guard. "His uncle ran after him with a knife and he bolted up here at once. Bellomo found him at the entrance this morning." Bellomo is the chief porter.

"How many are you, in your family?"

"Ten. Thirteen with my mother, and my uncle and grandmother."

"Are none of them in work?"

"Only my uncle, when he's not ill." His nervous twitching had lessened, but it was hard to tell what he was like: good or bad, intelligent or stupid. It was clear that, having obtained his interview, he now expected a job. Silence reigned again.

The Signorina tried once more. "Now you have spoken with the doctor," she said. "Now we all know you. As soon as there is a place for you, we will send for you. Now go." He did not go.

"You must go now." Even the guard did not move.

"Tell your uncle that if he beats you, he'll have to answer for it to us."

"Isn't there a job for me at once?" stammered Ugo, in a voice grown suddenly loud. "My uncle wants me to have work at once. He won't see me again if I'm not working here."

"Your uncle is crazy," exclaimed the Signorina. The guard took him again by the arm. The Signorina went up the stairs to the floor above, and I sat down in the entrance hall on a chair near the panelled wall. The guard was supporting Ugo by one arm, while he stared at the ground. The Signorina came down after a while, and put some money into his hand. "Go back to your uncle," she said. The guard pushed him gently away.

"You see how it is, Doctor? I'm glad that you've seen him, too," said the Signorina.

"Perhaps he is ill." The strong mid-day light from the sea was already heralding the lunch-hour break. Since I was about to go away for some weeks, to our headquarters in the north, I begged the Signorina to arrange a medical interview for him. "Let's do that, at least. Even before taking him on. At once. Even if we don't take him on."

She gave me a sharp but kindly glance, rather surprised. I explained: "One can see how it will end."

"When they have their medical interview they are sure that they'll start work next day. It's worse for them, Doctor, they deceive themselves. We aren't a hospital . . ."

"But let us make this one exception, Signorina, let us two for once make this exception."

But perhaps we shall not make it, in order to keep to the rules, or out of slackness, or from cowardice.

CHAPTER VI

MAY. Tuesday

RETURNING FROM THE north after many weeks I found the guards, led by Bellomo himself, in a state of ferment. They had been applying a new regulation about the cleaning of the factory in such a manner as to be accused by the workers of "creating the atmosphere of a barracks".

The new regulation had been prompted by the number of greasy marks on the building's colour-washed walls and the rubbish left about the mown lawns of the garden and round the sinuous lines of the ornamental pool. Many of the workers take their hot lunch from the canteen to eat out of doors; in fine weather the place seems to be one great picnic.

The management had authorized the guards to impose fines, and they had been fining ruthlessly, either out of pride in maintaining the cleanliness of an exceptional factory or from a wish to defend their fellow-southerners from the usual accusations of slovenly habits.

I had to see a worker who had been fined more than the rest and was most embittered against the guards. A lad from the stamping section came up, with a gold chain at his neck, his hair combed into a tuft, tight trousers under his overalls and elegant shoes, with which he worked the pedal of one of the lighter presses at the rate of one thousand five hundred times an hour.

How was it that he was eating his lunch in the garden this morning? Why not enjoy the sun afterwards, for a siesta? "I wasn't eating in the garden," he said rebelliously. "They have made the place like a barracks. I just came out chewing."

The man who does the running-in of the calculators had disappeared from the assembly-lines, having been transferred, with his work, to the lower floor, as a punishment. He had been courting one of the girls of the testing department, who had been trying to shake him off for a year. A brother of hers was learning the easy stages on the lower floor, too.

One morning towards the end of April a new calculating machine continued to make a mysterious error, and all the charge-hands and mechanics were busying themselves around it. Suddenly the man from the running-in accused the girl of having spoilt the machine: he had seen her himself, working the keys as though her mind were wandering, and staring about her in an improper way. At this—the man had spoken loudly—the girl's brother rushed up from the other end of the room; the runner-in awaited him, standing firmly in the midst of his buzzing machines, and struck him full in the face.

Thursday

The works committee has asked for a crucifix to be placed in the dining-hall. They also want Italian popular music relayed to the assembly lines in addition to records of orchestral works and American jazz (regarded by the management as more educative). And they ask that the passing from one grade to another should be speeded up.

Friday

One of the group of applicants who stand about every morning at the entrance threw himself today under the Manager's car, when we were all, at about two o'clock, in the dining-room.

Saturday

On the Manager's big writing-table the usual ash-tray was standing, full of cigarette-ends. He always surrounds himself with this aroma of cigarette smoke and is rather intimidating, with his intelligent, comprehending, but somewhat mysterious air. He gives extraordinary attention to every problem, great or small, but seems to hide behind a barrier of shyness, as though continually perplexed or unsatisfied. He makes no sign of having understood one's problems, not even by so much as a nod of his head; but his subsequent actions show how very well he has done so, together with his references to others of his staff, and to the factory.

From the affair of the fines we went on to questions concerning the grades of work, and the timing—still the heart of the production problem—and also to the functions of a personnel office in relation to the technical staff: in other words, problems of *staff organization* and *line organization*. In the philosophy of industry, these correspond with subject and object in moral philosophy.

It seems, in the Manager's room, that this question dominates the factory's whole outlook, and with it one's view of society and history. When he outlines the plan of future productivity our work appears like a ship under full sail. We are to make new products, and, with them, face all the risks of the market.

Unfortunately, the workers come to believe that they are with us simply in order, blindly, to make thousands, millions of parts all alike; and we feel that we are only here to engage a few of them and say no to a whole population.

The Manager did not mention the man who yesterday threw himself under his car. He asked, however, that an eye should be kept on those who stand about the entrance. They have all had negative answers to their requests for work, either following their examinations or simply on application, but every morning they hang about in groups before the gates. It is impossible to drive them away.

"It would be best for you to speak to them all, just once, and one at a time."

This business of interviews and examinations holds up the starting of any new work in the factory: for those already engaged have to be interviewed too, their output estimated, any change of job checked up on, and difficult cases considered.

"For the next year, it's the men outside who matter" declared the Manager. "Have patience. Either we interview them, or we close the gate and put the police there."

"I'll see them all . . ."

"It's a necessity."

Already there was a heap of cards on my table, sent up from the entrance, with the names of the applicants wanting to see me. Motive "personal". Which is perfectly correct, since their reasons are always personal and they always want the personnel office.

The porter from our floor was missing, and the men were in consequence all crowded into the small waiting-room. I called out the first name, through the Signorina's room, which joined the waiting-room.

"Vincenzo Accettura!"

The name penetrated the head of the Signorina, who sat back from her type-writer and laughed. "Ah, so with the new methods Accettura too is coming up. He's an old acquaintance of ours, the one who threw himself under the Manager's car. He's been waiting at the entrance for a year. You'll have an interesting interview, Doctor."

Accettura came in triumphantly, with a sprightly, knock-kneed gait. He crossed the brightly lit room, stiffly moving one arm up and down, at the end of which a hand with only two fingers was curled round a hook. He was a little man, dressed in black, with a wrinkled face, one side of it paralysed, and he moved jerkily because his leg, too, was paralysed on the same side as his arm and his face.

Approaching, he muttered something incomprehensible and

threatening, as he made awkward movements in my direction. I said
to him, "Sit down, Accettura."

With a serious and important air he took a chair, surprised at the
invitation. For a moment he was silent, as though bewildered. Then he
pulled himself together, and began, rapidly and in an unknown dialect,
to address me; fearing, it seemed, that he would be unable to unburden
himself wholly and in time, before someone chased him away.

A stream of words poured out, in a dialect cut, as it were, in two,
of which one part remained in his mouth and the other came out, but
all confused. I listened to him for a while in a kind of mental darkness,
waiting for some phrase upon which to seize in its entirety. He was
shaking the hook on his stiff arm, clawing the air. His disordered
speech resolved itself, by dint of continual repetition, into a complaint
that I at last understood: "You won't give me work because I threw
myself under the Manager's car. But I didn't want to fall, I wanted to
stop it."

"I'm ready to believe you, Accettura."

"Ah, you believe me?"

He stopped speaking, astonished. "It is the police, not you, who
have made such a to-do about it. Just like the police. And now you
won't consider me, because I wanted to speak to the Manager? But
if you believe me, you can give me a job. I can work well, with my
other hand." He laid his good hand on the table. "Is it wrong for a
civilized man to stop and speak to a Manager? But you are better than
the police. You've let me come up here, for the sake of justice. This
hand is good, Doctor."

I looked at it, until he drew it back, hiding the other.

"It's not your accident, Accettura. You must not think that. It's
true that you should not have thrown yourself under the Manager's
car. But we are taking on no more workers here." Was he deaf, or
did he understand?

He wriggled on his chair, and started on another stream of incomprehensible words.

"The factory, Accettura, has its own rules. We are working here
not for today, nor for tomorrow . . . We can take on applicants only
when there is a place free . . . We cannot take a man if there is no
room for him. Where would we put him? Just to wait somewhere
until a place should become empty? A factory like ours hasn't one
place too many or too few. It's the rule of the organization."

It was impossible to know whether he understood or not; but anyway he was determined to be blind and deaf in defending his right to

have made merely a well-meaning mistake in stopping the Manager, a mistake which, he thought, had caused him to be rejected by us. He was quick to repent: "Yes, I ought not to have done it. I'm sorry . . ."

"It is the rule of the organization," I repeated, my mouth dry. "It is a question of production. The factory functions only because the organization looks to the future. Now, the organization—no one, not the Manager, nor his chief, nor the President of the whole company, in northern Italy, can do anything about it—the organization prevents us from taking on more workers. It prevents us from engaging you, Accettura." To speak of the funnel to him would be useless, he would want to be the one to go through it.

He replied gravely: "You are quite right, Doctor."

"If you throw yourself under the Manager's car, Accettura, does that change the rules of the organization? If the Manager had gone over you and injured you, would that have made it easier to give you work? Would that have opened up a job in the factory for you? A place in the factory becomes free when production increases and we need new men. But production increases and we need more men only if the organization is perfect and we haven't one man too many." I paused for breath, and then sought an example. "We are not a ministry, where the organization is elastic, one of those ministries, you know, at Rome, where they can add another table . . ."

He repeated: "You are quite right, Doctor."

"A table that costs them nothing," I went on, trapped by his reasonable demeanour into talking too much. "Here instead of tables we add machinery costing millions of *lire*. And even a worker represents capital."

"Oh, yes, the cost is great, you are quite right, Doctor." This time he spoke with a look of wistful humility.

"It costs a lot . . ." he reflected, as though by spending his days at the gate-keeper's lodge he knew the organization as well as we did.

"You understand, Accettura? If it were for me to decide . . . But I haven't the power . . ."

"You are quite right," he said again. "But I am starving, Doctor. Starvation is hard to bear."

"I know, I know . . . I know . . ."

The Signorina looked round the door for a moment, signing to me. Catching sight of her, he took fright.

"Accettura, we will help you in some way."

"No, no, Doctor, I don't want charity from you. You have done me the honour of receiving me. But I shall have to go on bothering you. Ten thousand *lire* only last a fortnight. And after that? I beg you to give me a permanent post, even cleaning out the lavatories, so that I haven't got to worry you any more. I am starving, Doctor."

"Have you worked before?" He became animated, and waved his good arm. "Of course I have worked. I have worked a great deal. I was guard at a factory, and no one passed the gates without my seeing who it was. They discharged me because of the war . . . Later they let me hang about, and they gave me soup."

"But they never re-engaged you?"

"Oh, no, just promises that came to nothing. They discharged all the custodians. You can take me on as anything—labourer, watchman, messenger."

"But how many watchmen do you think we need, Accettura? More watchmen than workers, more lavatories than workers?"

"You're quite right, Doctor. But I am starving. It's not easy to put up with hunger." Gloomily he moved his hook beneath the table.

"You live alone?"

"Yes, my mother is dead. I live under the road here."

"In a house?"

"No, under the road." Below the wall of the main road, on the cliff-side, there are some caves. He leant forward, pleased to be questioned as to his address.

"I have explained to you, Accettura, we cannot give you a job."

He waved his hook, and his mind returned to the subject of the car. "You want to punish me because I threw myself . . ."

"No, no, Accettura."

"You are quite right, Doctor." He began again to repeat all his arguments, which I had not understood at the beginning, but now knew only too well. "I am starving."

"I understand, Accettura, but I can do nothing."

"Shall I go to the Manager?" He rose to his feet. I did the same, and said to him: "There's nothing the Manager can do."

"Then shall I go to the President, Doctor? Or to Rome, to the Prime Minister?" He knew about the Prime Minister. But not waiting for my reply, he went staggering from the room.

Saturday

After I had seen seven applicants and said no to them all, a young girl, nervous but affected, sat before me, and began speaking at once as though she were in a great hurry: "Doctor, we are in such great need. My father is a skilled hand at the engineering works, but he only brings home ten thousand *lire* a month. The rest goes in deductions because we are so many children."

"What do you mean? That he manages to get sums in advance?"

"Not in advance, in deductions."

"But what deductions? You mean that the pay he ought to bring home in a lump sum, he draws gradually, beforehand?"

"Oh, no, Doctor, he brings home ten thousand *lire*."

"Ten thousand *lire* for a whole month?"

"Yes, ten thousand *lire* a month," she insisted, in her sing-song dialect.

"Signorina, it's not possible, I don't believe it." Her small head was lowered in mortification. Every now and then these fair-haired girls turn up whom one would take for foreigners, if it weren't that they speak the local dialect. She was wearing a woollen cardigan and a skirt, and low-heeled white shoes; in fact, she was dressed as she would be at home, or for the beach.

"It's not possible. A skilled workman cannot earn only ten thousand *lire* a month. There's some mistake."

"You don't believe me, then, Doctor? I am lying?" She was ready to burst into tears. I had to stop her crying.

"You are not lying, of course, Signorina, but why don't you explain?"

"It's because there are so many of us, all the money goes in deductions," and she bent her head again.

"I should have thought," I smiled, "that with so many children he would have been paid more than the others, because he would have more allowances."

She gave me a confidential glance. "No, Doctor, he doesn't bring home more family allowances than the others. That's how it is. He has less than the others. That's why I need to work. I could do some job, Doctor, even cleaning the lavatories."

"We employ very few women here," I said, unsmilingly. "And soon we shan't have work for those we have. We are getting some electrical plant that will replace them."

"It's not true, Doctor," she retorted self-confidently. "They're not so few. I know many of them, Maria Garofalo and . . ."

"So you think you know better than I do?"

"No, Doctor, of course not. But you wouldn't find me a bad worker."

"We wouldn't know where to put you, Signorina. We have no need of more women." She sighed, looking at her bare hands. "There's nothing for me, then?" She was smiling and crying together. How was I to send her away, helpless as she seemed, without stockings, without a purse?

The last one waiting to be interviewed sent her away by coming in unannounced; not having been summoned he made no bones about presenting himself: "I am Giovanni Giglio. Have you called me?" The girl rose like a feather and drifted away as the massive Giovanni Giglio approached. "Doctor . . ." she murmured for the last time, walking backwards.

By the time I had got rid of Giglio, it was late. The strong, mid-day light indicated that we had reached the end of the week, and that all the workers had left the building. On Saturday they do not eat in the canteen.

The reflection from the sea was white, and invaded the entrance hall. Here a stout priest was standing, and asking for a lift into Naples: could someone drive him at least as far as San Rocco, to the bus stop? "Yes, I can." Perspiring, he followed me at once to my car, so bewildered that he hardly thanked me; he was the uncle of one of our workers, and had come from Torre to see him. "Do you know my nephew, Giovanni di Giovanni?" he asked, panting.

"Father, there are so many of us here. Do you know where he works?"

"I'm not sure . . . Somewhere on the ground floor, over to the left here."

"In the workshop?"

"It may be the workshop. He likes it very much."

He had to squeeze himself into my small car, which he managed to do backwards, hoisting himself on to the seat and then drawing up his legs; once in, though still panting, he declared in a more authoritative voice: "He's a good boy, you'll be pleased with him. I can answer for him. I baptized him myself."

"That's all right, Father." We started to make our way past the white columns of the portico. But from the entrance-hall the Manager, his hair *en brosse*, suddenly appeared, the last to leave the building; followed by his chauffeur, he went over to his big black car, and I slowed down in order to let him leave first.

"It's the Manager." The priest nodded approvingly at my gesture of deference.

"He, too, is a good man," he said thoughtfully, as we went down the curved drive towards the gate-keeper's lodge, now finally deserted after my clean sweep this morning.

"A very good man."

"This factory has come to relieve our need. It is a work of mercy," said the poor country priest, settling himself in his seat. "It has had the Bishop's blessing, and, if you will allow me to say so, Doctor, it has mine too. You are a doctor, aren't you? Or an engineer?"

"A doctor."

"A doctor," he said, with his head bowed, his hands on his knees, strong in his profound spiritual authority: an authority that the humblest priest, of the lowest status, can always, when he wishes, exhibit here, like a claw. "I will tell my nephew of your kindness."

"So your nephew likes his work? Is he on the automatic lathes?"

"I couldn't say. I don't know about that, but he is a good boy, and grateful."

"That's all right, Father."

"I am only a poor priest, I have to return home on foot. But Giovanni listens to what I say. He always shows respect for religion, and for his relations and those in authority over him."

"They are all respectful."

"They should be, always. It is only right," he responded, as though still conscious of his own power over people's souls, and ready to use it in alliance with that of the doctor beside him.

But what was the Manager's chauffeur doing, why didn't he move off? The car was crawling towards the porter's lodge at a snail's pace, despite the signals made by Bellomo, who, impressive as ever, was indicating with a traffic policeman's gestures that the road was clear. Indeed, having reached the gates, the driver pulled up abruptly, and I had to jam on my brakes with my car almost touching the bumpers of the other. Di Giovanni's uncle was jerked forward against the windscreen.

Bellomo came up to the window of the Manager's car, removing his cap in order to lean inside, with an anxious expression. "Yes, yes, I'll see to it." He was given some order. "It's quite all right, sir." Then he straightened himself, to scrutinize the main road again. There was nobody sitting on the low wall backing on to the sea. Usually, the applicants either hover round the gate-keeper's lodge, worrying the guards, or, when tired after hours of waiting, sit on the wall in the shadow of the pines, to watch the factory officials going in and out. The wall is public property.

As Bellomo, again signalling that the way was clear, withdrew into his glazed cabin, the driver accelerated confidently, and I followed. We were half-blinded by the glare and indeed half-dazed by fatigue and hunger, for it was already two o'clock. The Manager must have been absorbed by his thoughts.

Like a scarecrow, a dry branch covered in rags, Accettura was standing between a column and an oleander bush, where our pavement joined the main road. Bellomo, who could not see him from his cabin, although, as we discovered later, he had passed the whole morning only a stone's-throw away, had thought him safe in his den beneath the road.

Slowly, in low gear, the Manager's car took the curve on to the main road, while I kept a few yards between my car and his. I had not left the drive before Accettura sprang from his hiding-place and crossed right in front of the black car.

Before the bumper hit him he raised his good arm, and like a plucked bird with one wing extended, made as though to dive under the radiator. The driver instantly brought the car to a standstill, and I did the same with mine.

Accettura, gabbling excitedly, slipped round the radiator in order to reach the Manager's window. The chauffeur, pale in the face, had not time to get out before Bellomo had leapt from his cabin and seized Accettura by his good arm.

The car shot away at once, and the highway remained empty in the glare from the sea, except for Accettura and Bellomo, who was grasping him by the arm as if he were an old woman. I changed down into low gear to turn the corner and to escape towards the city, without looking at the priest; while Bellomo waved his free arm energetically to me, as though to say, Go on, Doctor, quickly. We passed close by them: Bellomo touched his cap to me, to show that he was perfectly calm, but his teeth were chattering. Agitated, but unafraid, Accettura —trying to attract my notice—was shouting in his curious dialect.

"Doctor!" The word penetrated into my car, from the window beside the priest. "Excuse me, just a word, Doctor."

I slowed up, but Bellomo would not let go of him; he dragged him away, along the pavement, holding him firmly. The priest could make nothing of the incident. "If they end up under the wheels of a car . . ." he said, but fell silent again. I hesitated, uncertain whether to stop or not, and then drove off.

CHAPTER VII

Monday

IT HAS BEEN a memorable morning for Dioguardi, one of our men, who is a member of the works committee and was formerly a music-hall performer.

We have to have a reception office, because of the stream of visitors to the factory—foreign tourists, journalists, ministers, sociologists and architects. This morning, the well-known Sicilian actor Eduardo De Filippo announced that he was coming to see us. Naturally, Dioguardi, diminutive and vivacious, with his head full of comic songs and mad ideas, was picked out to accompany him as a guide.

Towards eleven o'clock, the appointed hour, Dioguardi and one of the engineers solemnly left their work and went to the entrance-hall to meet De Filippo. The factory was seething with impatience. The workers were waiting for the tragic and comic masks to appear together in the workshops, to walk round the machines and to pause at the benches for a few words. Visitors to the factory always follow an established route—workshops, machine-rooms, assembly-lines; and then issue on to the terrace in front of my room to admire the view.

They awaited his coming as that of a father. But this idolized symbol of their freedom and of the theatre—their love for which finds little outlet with us—was late in appearing. It was known that, at a quarter past eleven, he had entered the gates. Yet he still did not come: was he only going to visit the social services and the garden, or was he closeted with the Manager, or had Dioguardi perhaps cornered him with a view to joining his company?

Instead, De Filippo, with the engineer and Dioguardi, was stuck in the lift. He had gone straight to it, because he wanted to start with the assembly-lines and the finished articles. He declared that in that way he would understand better what we were making.

We have a smart new lift, polished and shining, but it is the only piece of machinery in the factory that every now and again goes wrong: it opens and shuts automatically, but even on the day of our inauguration it stopped halfway. This time it stuck a yard or so from the first floor.

I was not there myself; I was frantically searching among the applications in my office for a radio-mechanic, without success, because the skilled men are never to be found when they are wanted.

A mechanic had to be called up to work the lift by hand. Meanwhile De Filippo, imprisoned within the four lightly panelled walls, maintained a calm and philosophic attitude, though he was somewhat ironic, in a courteous way, about the weaknesses of modern technical progress. Despite their close quarters and the lack of air, they all waited imperturbably, Dioguardi delighted at spending so long a time in close proximity with his guest.

At last De Filippo, with his escort, issued calmly from his prison, and went to greet the Manager, blinking his eyes in the blazing light that invades the office. He then set off for the assembly-lines. The men in the tool-shop were frantic: if he did not get to them before midday, we were clearly going to have a strike in reverse, for they would remain at work instead of rushing off to the canteen. Their hunger was forgotten as they waited for their idol to appear.

At the first of the assembly-lines, a photographer, walking backwards, was taking photographs by flashlight of the visitor and his guides, amongst whom Dioguardi always figured. This upset the workers. They were quite ready to wait for De Filippo at their benches and to carry on with their work so long as he stopped beside each one; but that some should be photographed with him, and others not, was more than they could stand.

In the effort to be taken at his side, and to attract his notice, they leant from the benches, holding their machine parts still in their hands, and assuming the most irresistibly comical expressions. Perhaps, who could tell, when De Filippo saw the photographs, he might discover some hidden talent, here or there, and would snatch them away from the assembly-lines to act with him . . . Our workers have a passionate love for the stage, which to them is a kind of paradise lost.

But De Filippo—so Dioguardi recounted afterwards—was discouraging about the theatre. He would not talk about it. Like the engineer of a rival firm, so said Dioguardi, he was only interested in the timing of the stages and the hourly production. And even Dioguardi, following the footsteps of his god—Dioguardi, who had been fined twice for "deliberately provoking excessive hilarity among his fellow-workers"—maintained an official air. He was simmering with suppressed *vis comica*, but he spoke gravely of "groups", "sub-groups" and "assemblage". At each bench a new stage opened before him, a new platform; but the great actor, in a toneless voice, only asked questions about the work that was being done, and seemed bent on following our manufactures from their earliest state to their completion; finding in the men of the south a love of work similar to his own. Even if his own labours were not industrial, he wanted his admirers, southerners like himself, to understand that they must persevere in this new way of life. He realized their nostalgia for other things, but, a little sadly, he seemed to be telling them to be sensible, that the theatre was not enough; while aloud he commented, full of admiration, "Well done. How quick you are. It's amazing." Not once did the crowing cock of the drill dare to lift up its voice. With his emaciated mask of a face, the very symbol of the southerner's dignified, pathetic sadness, De Filippo went on towards the tool-shop.

Here he was much struck by the noise, the rhythm. The workers at the machines followed him about, silently, their eyes expressing their passionate devotion. He understood their feelings, and fearing to create some disorder, asked the photographer to keep away. According to Dioguardi, there was a moment when De Filippo, about to leave the tool-shop, was on the point of stopping to give them a recitation. But his heart failed him. "He opened his mouth. Then he shut it again. We didn't hear the golden voice. We must have frightened him," declared Dioguardi, regretfully. When he told De Filippo about the entertainment that was being planned for the workers—"an entertainment organized by the works committee, a really smart show, on professional lines"—De Filippo only said, "That's splendid," and slipped away quickly, not to disturb them further.

His face appeared suddenly behind the panes of my window on to the terrace. He was surrounded by two engineers, a clerk and two girl secretarial workers. One of the latter pointed out the island to him, and he gazed at it thoughtfully. Dioguardi returned, and said to him: "You can't think what beautiful sunsets we see, of an evening."

"Ah, you can see the sun setting, even from the workshops?" asked De Filippo, gently. "You still notice the sunsets?"

Dioguardi went back into the building, and returned with a cup of coffee for the great actor. He held it out to him as though in homage. De Filippo turned, to take it; and in drinking, glanced thoughtfully into my room, with a look of surprise, as though the curtain had gone up. Then he hurriedly took his leave.

An atmosphere of melancholy lay over the factory for the rest of the day, of nostalgia for the art of the theatre.

It gets dark in the evening now, after work. From the crossroads on the highway a long road goes winding down to Santa Maria. At one turn of it, on the hill, one can look down on the old fortress and the sea, but in the evening one can only see the lights of the bay on the horizon. The clothes hanging out to dry are invisible against the sky and the children scatter before my car, a blur in the darkness. Since the Commune has instituted a by-pass, with the idea of speeding up the traffic, one has to take a steep side-road down to the town, over a level-crossing that is always closed. When at last the train has passed and the barriers have been raised, the little town lies before one, round the temple with its columns in the mud, round the green garden in its midst; with the lights of the piazza, and the edge of the port, and the sea beyond.

I had taken a turn on foot, to buy bread and fruit for supper. A small town does not wake up, as a city does, in the evening; indeed, after sunset, having no entertainments, it seems at its most quiet. The daily hubbub of a continual market, the flow of people this way, that way, in and out of the houses, in and out of the shops, suddenly dies down. This is typical of life in the south, of that chronic feverish animation that becomes stilled in the evening.

All the same, at Santa Maria it always seems to be a holiday, with the teeming population, the carts, the booths piled with vegetables and fish, the sale of ices and lemonade. The sun shines gloriously upon it by day, and the nights are sweet with sea breezes. In the narrow alleys there is no traffic; old women sit at their doorways, artisans are at their work and children at play.

The men, on the other hand, who are unemployed and possessed of initiative, our candidates, in fact, usually prefer the open spaces, the piazza, the gardens, the railway station or the port.

I had stopped my car near the port, and four small boys immediately surrounded it. But there was also a man, unknown to me, with the face of a clerical worker, about forty years old, wearing a white shirt buttoned up at the neck, but no tie. He bowed, shyly and very politely. "You remember me? I had meant to come up for a second interview . . . I ought to have replied . . . I wanted to say, I would come even as a manual worker. I would be glad of any kind of job."

"As a manual worker it would be difficult to place you, if you are on the list of clerical applicants." He looked astonished. "Then as a clerical worker. Can I apply at once as a clerical worker?"

"That is impossible now, because we are not engaging any clerical workers at all, at present."

"But . . ."

"You see, there is no possibility of work. It's nothing to do with me."

He thought over my words, and bent his head in mortification. "But you do remember me, Doctor?"

"I remember you now. You came the day before yesterday." He sighed, and remained standing beside me.

I walked a few paces from the car, along the sea, where a line of lamps set up reflections from the boats in the black water. He followed me. "Can you give me any hope?" he asked, but as though he were not asking for himself.

"I can give you hope, but what good is that?" He grinned: "Oh, Doctor, if you give me hope . . . it's something. A word from you . . ."

"Well, I can give you hope. But it's nothing to do with the factory. I can't prevent anyone from hoping. That doesn't change the situation in the slightest degree."

He raised his arms: "Doctor, if you only would, just a word from you . . ."

"No. But do you know what we can both hope? That the factory will grow. That it will become so big that it can employ thousands of workers, hundreds and hundreds of clerks . . ."

"Who can wish it more than I do, Doctor? I hope that it will become very big indeed." He spread out his arms, as though to embrace the whole hillside, the town, the beaches. He pretended to be enthusiastic—and perhaps he was—about the future of the factory.

But meanwhile the walk was not being fruitful; he looked dejected. "You will not forget me?"

"Very well, I will not forget you." Another was waiting for me by the rose-coloured houses, beneath one of the lamps at the entrance to an alley. He waited as if he were on a queue, but as one who, though with a similar request, feels superior to the rest. He did not want to get mixed up with the clerk.

The clerk went off towards the piazza, returning to his "building negotiations", as he had described his occupation on his form. The other was walking up and down in the black mud of the port. If one turns one's back on this ill-smelling quarter, the briny air reminds one of the beauty of the Bay at night. And it is precisely by night that one sees the factory standing out most clearly on the hillside above the town, like a long castle of glass, lit by its fluorescent lights. The inhabitants of the coast and the fishermen can see it, in all its unapproachability, from every part of the Bay. The wooded hillside is no longer one of those excrescences on the volcanic landscape that strike the tourists and leave the natives cold, but the abode of a forbidden palace. It is there that one can have a safe job, in the midst of clean machinery;

it is there that one can have a bath every day, and that one acquires honour among one's fellow-citizens. No more fishing by lamplight, no more picking up work on the bathing beaches in summer, only to be unemployed all the rest of the year.

The big, dark man who was waiting for me approached. He was wrapped in a dark blue overcoat with yellow stripes, and had a yellow tie and eyes that gleamed yellow in the lamplight. "Excuse me, just a word," he said, in a thick voice. "I am waiting for a reply from you."

"We never reply by word of mouth. You will have a letter."

"Please, Doctor. You answer me without knowing what it is I want to say. Perhaps you don't know who I am. I am the medical assistant."

"We have no need of help in our sick-room."

There wasn't another soul about the port. In a threatening tone he went on: "You don't take me seriously . . . Why haven't you . . .?"

"I don't take you seriously?" I interrupted angrily. He took no notice. "Why am I not summoned for the examinations, Doctor?" he asked, coming closer. "I don't need recommendations. I'm the best medical assistant in the town. When someone is dying they call me in, not a doctor. They send for me."

"Have you your diploma?"

"I'm better than that." He glanced at my car, and then at the alley-way behind him. "I'm respected here."

"That's all right. We'll respect you too."

"But if you don't summon me for the examinations . . ." He had become bolder. "You can't respect me without proof. You don't even know how I do an intermuscular injection, or an intravenal one. Do you want to discredit me?"

"Our examinations are not concerned with . . ."

"What are they concerned with? They are concerned with your promise, your conscience. I am not like the others . . . Perhaps you haven't understood . . ." He raised his head like a bull.

"Why? I don't make promises." But if I had? When one sits glued to one's chair for hours, sometimes one cannot help leaving a chink of hope open for them: I murmur that perhaps in a year's time . . . and then they come back next day, like this. The man glimpsed a weakness on my part, and followed it up, cunning and querulous. "You don't take me seriously, but why? Why? Everyone knows me here. I must do the tests, I must. I have to show them . . ."

Bulky in his big coat, he leaned forward again. "In my position I have a right, a right to do the examinations." With increasing irritation he went on, "If I don't, they won't call me in any more. Can't you have me summoned for tomorrow?" There was something sinister in the way he kept looking round him. Was someone coming? There was nobody about; the last boat had left the jetty, and the festive, holiday-making Santa Maria crowd neglected this strip of ground beneath the fortress with its dirty water and narrow alleys like the openings of drains.

"But if we have no need of a medical assistant?" I asked, turning back towards my car. He said: "I know that you have need of one. I know it from your doctor's assistant, when she comes down to Santa Maria to buy medicine. She has too much work, she can't manage it any more. And then, to have certain medicines, she rings at my door . . . Even the injections for your wife, it was I who got them."

"What injections?"

"The antilymphatic."

"Aren't they to be found in Santa Maria?"

"Not the strong kind. It was the strong that was needed, and the chemists here don't keep it." "But don't the chemists here order directly from the city?" "Oh, Doctor . . . the weak kind!"

"I'll speak to the assistant tomorrow."

He did not flinch: "Doctor, you need someone like me in your infirmary."

We made our way into the piazza that stretched along the sea. On the hillside the factory was shining more coldly with its bluish light, as the evening advanced; at that hour Bellomo was alone on guard, with the gates closed and the police-dog loose about the place.

"You know more about it than I do. If you know so much, you had better take my place, and interview people yourself."

"What are you saying, Doctor," he responded, with a magnanimous wave of the hand that did not conceal his sense of repulsion at not being either engaged by us or summoned for the examinations.

"Unfortunately, we have no need of you." The blow seemed to wind him.

"Everyone will know . . . that you have spoken to me . . . and then haven't thought me worth examining . . . No one would expect it . . ." he was muttering angrily.

"We can't put you to manual work. You have your profession. Do you want to throw it away?" His thoughts still seemed seething in his thick head. "You can't throw your profession away."

"I know who doesn't throw a profession away. Whoever has fifty thousand *lire*." I had my hand on the door of my car.

"Whoever has fifty thousand *lire* can get into the examinations and something more," he repeated.

"Who told you that? Prove it!"

"Eh, Doctor, as to proof, there is never proof. But there is a man in Santa Maria who can get you a place in the factory for fifty thousand *lire*."

"And I suppose the personnel office takes half, twenty-five thousand?"

He remained silent at my fury, unjust as it seemed to him, and waited for the indignation on my part to subside. Then he repeated hoarsely: "There's someone in Santa Maria, someone who goes about . . ." I had jumped into the car and slammed the door in his face. Starting up the engine, my wrath was reduced to a single thought: an enquiry, we must have an enquiry.

CHAPTER VIII

Tuesday morning

THE ENQUIRY THAT I wanted was already on foot. I learnt this at the interview I had urgently requested with the Manager, first thing this morning.

"Yes," he said, as soon as I had told him of the unsavoury affair that had come to my notice. "Yes," he repeated, annoyed, but perfectly calm. "There's a man, well-dressed, a blackguard who goes about the town. Did you see him yesterday evening? We don't know his name."

"I didn't see him. I was speaking to another man, who told me. It was dark."

"We have warned the Carabineers. They are waiting for proof."

"Are they waiting for us to supply them with proof? He must be some kind of private agent. We shall never discover who he is."

"Couldn't you find out his name?" asked the Manager in his practical way, not giving a thought to my state of mind.

"Who would come and tell me? Unless . . . He must have an accomplice here. He asks fifty thousand *lire* for obtaining a job in the factory and presumably shares it with the personnel office. When he comes . . . to offer twenty-five thousand *lire* to Signorina S. and me . . . We can then . . ."

The Manager's face did not change. The doubt cast, ironically but with dramatic force, upon the honesty of two of his staff—the indication of the suspicion and calumny to which we were exposed—disturbed him not at all. He merely said: "There have been some anonymous denunciations. Don't worry, go on quietly with your work. We'll try to get proof. You go on with your job."

"If the scoundrel were to approach us when we go down to the town . . ." I hoped that perhaps I might force him to give me some positive instructions.

"All the better. In that way, you could discover who he is. Just carry on and don't worry," he replied, in his dogged way. By now he knows well enough that as manager he must resist any temptation to let the emotional atmosphere of the south excite him; even if in so doing he runs a risk of under-rating its effects.

"Go on quietly with your job," he repeated courteously, as he signed for his secretary to bring in the head accountant. "Just carry on as usual."

According to the Signorina, if there is corruption in the personnel office, it has competition to face. Rumour has it that the only real way to get into the factory is through the Venetian mistress of one of our engineers. A Venetian, living at Santa Maria? This seems most extraordinary. "Venetian, Venetian," confirmed the Signorina, and a vision of auburn hair and a milk-white skin was promptly conjured up. We wondered which of our few engineers, serious chaps—recently married, and one of them now on his honeymoon—could possibly be hiding such a siren down in the town.

The trouble is that the rejected applicants simply cannot resign themselves to their fate. In our part of the coast, below us, almost on the beach, the engineering works are engaging no more men, in fact are laying off three hundred of them; further along the bay, at the naval dockyard, they are discussing the introduction of short time. The Lombardo factory near the lake has reached its full complement and is not taking on any more employees; there are some possibilities at the steel-works, it seems; possibilities that we all hope may materialize. But none at the cement works, where the men become coated in dust. And beyond the hill that divides us from Naples, things are worse: nearly all the factories are in a state of crisis.

During these days some workshops near the city have been closed down. The men who were thrown out of work demonstrated, under the eyes of the mobile police, before the windows of both the mayor and the prefect. Six of them were arrested: all of them fathers of families, with a total of more than thirty children between them.

Can it be that the key man, who promises jobs in our factory, is the medical assistant himself? Could he have decided to obtain a place with us in order to strengthen his position? Perhaps with fifty thousand *lire* he really has succeeded in getting someone in for some kind of job: once would be enough for him to be believed omnipotent. But what about the Venetian woman?

Industrial psychology can now operate in a pleasant atmosphere of scandal.

The paper carries news about the other factories, our neighbours here. Today they have printed two complaints put forward by girl workers in a tobacco factory. The Signorina read them out aloud for my benefit. "To the Procurator of the Republic, I, the undersigned, Anna Imperiale, aged 15, wish to make the following denunciation. On the 4th June, in the T.M. factory, I went to the lavatory, and one of the managerial staff, Signor Vescovio, tried to follow me in. I said:

What do you want? He said, Let me come in, and pushed the door, which I managed to shut in his face. He said, Hurry up, when you come out I'll sack you. When I came out he slapped my bottom and said, You can have a week's pay, and leave at once. Now I have been unemployed for a week. I demand Vescovio's punishment and compensation for my unemployment."—"I, Pia Testa, declare that Signor Vescovio of the factory where I work, wanted to make me stand on the arm of a chair in which he was sitting. I said, I don't want to get up for you to see my legs. He said, Don't be silly, it doesn't matter if I see your legs. Now he picks out the light work for me and my companions think I'm a bad girl."

The Signorina was still reading when the bell sounded for the midday break.

It is the hour in which Straniero, head of the works committee, saunters round the offices, instead of rushing off hungrily with the rest; often he is waiting to see the Manager, and in the meantime comes to visit us. As leader of the opposition, he has won for himself an official position, more like a member of the clerical staff than that of a worker, and our relations have become familiar. He roams round the tables and discusses things with me and the Signorina, although till now there has always been a certain reciprocal shyness between us, as we try to sum one another up.

At the last meeting of the works committee he had shown himself impatient, even violent. When the matter of rates and qualifications was about to come up, the Manager asked him if he would like an aspirin. But today there was another request on the agenda, put forward by Dioguardi, and connected with De Filippo's visit: permission to get up an entertainment in the factory before the heat of mid-summer. Dioguardi undertook to bring in a dozen girl dancers from Naples. Straniero was waiting to be received by the Manager to discuss the entertainment: the management had already given its permission, but rejected the dancers, and Straniero—as a member of the Catholic party, while Dioguardi is independent politically—did not mean to make difficulties over this.

He appeared at the door, cheerful, still wearing his overalls, and with his blue eyes dancing. He speaks jerkily, confusing some of his arguments; but his talk goes running on, hurriedly, persuasively.

"What news, Doctor?" he asked. Did he know of my encounter in Santa Maria yesterday evening, I wondered?

"They're bribing us . . ." I answered.

"Ah, Doctor," he said, lowering his deep-set eyes, thoughtfully.

"Doctor, there are unpleasant rumours going about."

"The Venetian woman in the town . . .?" Straniero moves about as he speaks, touching the edge of a table or a chair nervously, and it seemed that he was not listening. Flicking his fingers and glancing sideways at me, he announced in his nasal voice: "In Santa Maria they say that at first you had to have recommendations to get in here, but that now you can get a job by paying."

"Is the works committee taking this matter up?"

"According to union rules, the works committee doesn't deal with that sort of thing," said Straniero, nervously plucking at his shirt. "That is, the works committee ought, in fact, to check up on the engagement of personnel; in my opinion this should be one of its tasks. It ought to work alongside the management . . . Well, we needn't go into this question of control. I often ask myself what powers the works committee has, whether it has any at all. If the choosing of personnel is so important here, why have we nothing to do with it? Of course, we have faith in you, Doctor, we trust you . . ."

"You must set up an enquiry."

He laughed, nervously. "Doctor, what enquiry can you make with the poor devils?"

"It seems that the Signorina and I are taking twenty-five thousand *lire* for every man we engage, Straniero. Twenty-five thousand *lire* . . ." He stepped back, shocked, from my table.

"Twenty-five thousand *lire* are half a man's pay. When we've increased our labour force here by a hundred men, we shall have reached two million, five hundred thousand *lire*. The personnel office is getting rich, we can give ourselves a good time. Have you read in the press that at the tobacco factory the managers slap the girls on their behinds?" Straniero put his hands before his eyes.

"Doctor, Doctor," he exclaimed, ironically, but more and more troubled.

"There is a key man, in a blue suit, down at Santa Maria. No need for psychotechnical tests. Or for recommendations. A much simpler system. And the works committee approves?"

"Doctor," he exclaimed again, coming back to my table, "too many hopes have been raised in this office, too many hopes. It would have been better to shut the gates, and have done with it."

"But, anyway, do you know this species of private agent? Have you heard his name? Everyone knows everyone else in Santa Maria."

"I know him by sight . . ." muttered Straniero, rapidly. "It must be the same one . . ."

"Well then?"

He leant his elbow on the writing-table and stretched out a hand towards me: "Doctor, what do you want to do? Do you want to take away their hopes? Do you want to have him arrested? But no one will give his name away here. Do you want to take away all hope from them?" He looked me straight in the eyes.

"We leave hope to everyone. And to us, the hope of taking twenty-five thousand *lire*." Straniero raised himself from the writing-table and gave a short laugh.

"You're honest, Doctor. You come from northern Italy. But you must understand." Unexpectedly grave, he delivered his peroration, like an old trade unionist. "Here, outside our gates, they are desperate. What can you do, and what can the works committee do? Let it alone, Doctor. They are all living in a state of despair."

The morning was nearly over and the Manager summoned him.

Tall, thin and silent—almost stealthy—the woman who does the rooms came in to tidy up my office, while next door the Signorina was frantically tapping our negative replies on her typewriter. Our usual afternoon occupation.

The woman had moved the steel filing-cabinets and pulled out the registers; now she was putting them together again. A mass of papers was spread over the tables, on the chairs—even my own—and on the floor.

Order is kept in what concerns the examinations and the selected applicants, but here there was just a mass of begging letters, of cries of misery, chaos. Everybody sends one application, but many of them five, six, or seven. I tried not to tread on the papers, or to sit on them; but one slipped from the table, and, with its large handwriting, caught my eye and went to my heart, because it began: "Try to consider me. Do not leave me to my fate, write to me that it would be sad indeed to have a heart so hard that it cannot take pity on a poor unemployed young man, in such great need that God alone could tell you what it means. Write to me in your kindness and let me have a favourable reply."

There is a pleasant atmosphere in the small room of the social welfare assistant, when we gather there of an evening, after the welcome six-o'clock bell has released us. We go down the drive, like holiday-makers leaving their house in the pine-woods for the beach.

This room on the high road seems nearer to the sea and the town, and screened from the conflicting passions of the factory. This evening the welfare worker—a willing, level-headed girl—was sitting at her small writing-table, alone.

Our talk, as always, turned on the factory. We regretted the workers' reluctance to complain. They are afraid. As workers, though, ought they necessarily to complain? And are they really afraid? Perhaps this concentration of ours on unhappiness has become the vice of our profession as social workers. We can only give moral first aid, and we come on the scene after the harm has been done. On the other hand, the factory doctor, in his sacred white coat, robs us of our work: they go to him with their physical ills, or because of some accident, and they then reluctantly come out with their most secret anxieties. We are in a weak position and can do little in the way of prevention; it is the doctor who knows all about their neurasthenia, and about the miscarriages and the love-affairs. He is in close contact with the workers of both sexes within the factory and sees them in all their nakedness; whereas we social workers remain at a distance, using merely words, though they are words that are indispensable to them. The young assistant, who has a university degree, was waiting to see a former school-fellow of hers. Sooner or later all the workers come to her office, with requests of one sort or another.

"There are quite a number, here, who were at school with me," she said. "Look, here comes one of them."

He was a tall, fair-haired youth with a big nose and a long face, who works with a certain languid elegance at the stamping machines, keeping silent even if one pauses beside him. He was wearing a new jacket, and standing squarely on his feet; then lounged against the door, looking slowly about him.

"You left school to start work, didn't you, Pepe?" asked the assistant, with the air of an elder sister.

"To work with my uncle."

"What does your uncle do?"

"He's a shop-keeper."

"And what did you do?"

"I worked in his office."

"And now where do you work?" she asked, for my benefit.

"At the presses."

"You like it, Pepe? Didn't you prefer the office?"

"What office? No . . . I like the work here. But, Signorina, I need glasses, the doctor has ordered them for me."

"Are you straining your eyes?"

"Yes, my eyes ache, all day." Pepe drooped more than ever; the assistant made out a voucher for him.

"So you like the work? Do you need anything else now?"

"What else should I need, Signorina?" said Pepe quietly, giving her a meaning smile; and hastily left the room, with a polite inclination of his head.

"These secondary schoolboys, there's no understanding them," murmured the assistant.

The next to come was one of my former candidates, big Bonocore, whom we welcomed warmly. During his interview, some time ago, he had admitted to me that he was in sympathy with the political views of Saragat, and, rather surprised, I said to him: "Then you must be one of the very few Social Democrats of the south."

"Yes, Doctor," he replied with a modest air, "I am interested in politics." He was sitting at the interview with his big body firmly settled on his chair, his eyes large and bright. He had a firm mouth and the strong face of a man, although he was only twenty-four years old, and there was self-reliance underlying the shy intelligence with which he answered my questions. He had waited to become engaged to a girl until all five of his sisters had been married off. It would take him two hours every morning to reach the factory from Torre, and two hours every evening to go home; he would have to cross Naples twice, take the tram, the train, and then do a stretch of the way on foot. "Won't you find the journey boring?"

"No, not if I am working here. And I can always read in the train."

"Ah, so you are a reader?"

Full of hope, he had started work, proud of his responsibility, ever thoughtful in his manner. The other day I saw him at the benches. Seated with others in a row he was hammering thousands of identical little metal plates, giving each one of them two or three blows with a hammer to smooth them out, work that was elementary but a timed stage in the mass-production. One might have thought he would find it degrading; that he, with his calm, almost professorial air, had been given nothing better than a toy to play with. What was the reflective, politically minded Bonocore thinking about, now that he had finally got into the factory?

He, too, had need of glasses; he was asking the assistant for them shyly: "Signorina, I am straining my eyes." Perhaps his spirit, strong like his body, was mortified by the monotony of the tiny plates that had to be adjusted by the tips of his fingers, while the rest of his big body remained unused on the chair.

He took his voucher and turned to go.

"Did you see all right before?"

"It's hard to know, Doctor."

"You find the work at the benches tires your eyes?"

"A little, Doctor."

"How do you like this mechanical work? It doesn't bore you?"

He smiled, showing small white teeth: "It amuses me, Doctor."

Often in the evening Straniero lingers under the covered way with its white columns among the pine trees, and waits for the social welfare assistant to finish her work; for he likes to leave the factory last.

A group of us, the assistant, the secretary of the works committee and I were walking along the road by the empty factory this evening, enjoying the fresh air. Straniero, his overalls discarded, was hovering uncertainly round me. The badge of the Christian-Democrat party was displayed in the button-hole of his jacket.

I asked him, suddenly: "You people of the works committee, Straniero, do you know the other factories hereabouts? Or do you stay shut up in our citadel?" Beyond the wall of the high road one could see the big engineering works below, along the beach; and there are a number of others to be found among the Roman remains, the ports, the volcanic lakes and extinct volcanoes of the coast. Immediately behind us, at the back of this intricate, convoluted land fringing the Bay, the dead, calcified country, subject to earthquakes, has thrown its inhabitants on to the industrial seaboard.

"I know all the factories. Do you want to visit them? I'll take you. I'll take you to the steel-works tomorrow if you like. It's a stronghold of the Reds, but there's nothing to be done about that, the works committee is in the hands of the Communists . . . They're all manual workers there, they spend their lives at the furnaces. Who do you expect them to vote for, with a life like that?"

"I don't know, Straniero. Why not for you, for the Catholic Party . . ."

"Eh, Doctor, we have different ideas, but we keep a united front. I'll take you to the steel-works, they're all friends of mine there." The girl from the welfare office grinned at him. "The Socialists and Communists are powerful. They have their premises in the factory itself, at the corner of the piazza. They occupied them after the Liberation and no one has had the courage to turn them out. They're high-handed, but you can't argue with men at the furnaces. We don't want

to, either. We have to pay for our premises, but they have taken over
those of the Fascists."

"Does no one try to dislodge them?"

"Dislodge them . . . with the heavy work they do, and all that dust"
—he became excited—"the dust . . . they're quite right, too. In all the
factories down there the Communists have a majority again. They're
so badly treated, you can't expect the Left to lose support. Bad conditions, and all that dust . . ."

"You think them right?"

"I don't think their ideas are right. But, Doctor, in these factories,
who is our enemy?" He was stumbling over his words again. "Who
is our enemy?" The assistant had walked on along the road once more.
"Are we against them or against the management? It's one or the
other." No one answered. He likes to play his part in a comedy, and
his blue eyes flickered as he looked at us. "Isn't it only fair that,
with the employers they've got, the Reds should be stronger than
we are?"

"If you think so." He wanted to drag me off at once to the steel-
works, perhaps partly to allay his disquiet at appearing as a friend of
the Reds; the disquiet that this fatal, fundamental unity provoked in
him.

"We'll go, we'll go. But it's too late, now. Good night, Straniero."

"Good night, Doctor." He became again the white revolutionary
who, after all, had confidence in his employers: the question of the
differences in grade does not divide us.

To reach my house I did not take the highway running along
the hill about halfway from the summit, but the coast road that winds
among the small houses of the summer bathers, and then across the
centre of Santa Maria. I hurried in order not to fall in with my medical
acquaintance of the other evening, pushing the country people who
would not get out of my way with the bumpers of my car. I then
continued between the sea and the deserted rocks, and the cliffs, edged
with prickly pear, on one of which stood our house, as far as
Castello. In the bare, untidy piazza, I rounded the corner of the steel-
works; the corner where the Social-Communists have their offices,
consisting of two dark dens in one of which some men could be seen
playing cards at grimy tables. Having taken the walled road by the
steel-works, I could hear the life of the factory rather than see it; but it
was all round me, and every now and then one could feel a blast of
hot air from the great furnaces. The railway makes the only breach in

the walls, with its level-crossing on the roadway, linking the foundries with the quay.

After Castello, a former military centre of the Bourbons, now crowded with civilian houses, I turned left, towards the main road, and passed beneath a railway bridge. Here there was a jumble of huts, of market gardens, and unfinished roads. Then came the tree-lined street of the Nato palaces, with American officers and N.C.O.s in their long, black cars. From here they go up to see the views from the upper city.

I, on the other hand, took the road towards the country, turning back on my tracks. It climbed the lonely hillside, and I turned my car at the wide parking-place near the top, with its four pine-trees. From here one could see the spur of Capo Grande on the sea, and the small near-by island; and lower down, the dark, narrow valley occupied by the steel-works. From above, its secrets are veiled by the yellow fumes, unceasingly exhaled; while flames from the great furnaces spurt here and there amidst the smoke.

From this viewpoint, foreigners from the north pause for their first sight of Naples. But in the evening it is full of Italian cars, with embracing couples sitting in the front seats, or hidden in the back, with jackets and cardigans hanging like curtains before the windows. I did not stop, but went on up the country lane leading to our small house, perched scarcely twenty paces from the edge of the cliff.

Before supper, having nowhere else to rest, I usually lie down on the big bed that occupies almost all our bedroom, my feet nearly reaching to the moon-lit terrace. There is complete silence, save for an occasional hoot from a ship in the port. But at eleven o'clock, when one should go to sleep, the siren for the night-shift goes off at the steel-works. After that one hears only periodic bangs and explosions from the furnaces. We are right out in the volcanic countryside, with its dry, terraced vineyards, on the crest of the hill above Santa Maria and the motor-road; and the lighthouse on the distant island sends out its beam at regular intervals to flicker weakly on our window-panes.

CHAPTER IX

Wednesday

At two o'clock last night, when we were all asleep, they were unloading a cargo of coal down at the pier, and filling the trucks belonging to the steel-works by means of a crane. The crane let a load drop on to the head of one of the steel-workers and killed him.

The news, which appeared in the morning paper, is not known by anyone either in the country round my house or here in the factory. It is always the same when anything serious happens in this industrial district. It seems that bad news gets lost among the vineyards or the waves of the sea.

Leaving the small garden of our house in the morning, I gave the pale, streaky sea a glance, and taking the lane that climbs up among the vineyards, crossed the summit in the teeth of a violent gale. From the little church of San Rocco the road goes down to the outlying parts of Santa Maria, crowded with children, women and carts: to the right, a hill conceals the dry lake of the Solfatara; to the left, the fortress rises on a hump of rock.

At the bottom of the hill, between the amphitheatre and our own housing-estate with its brightly coloured cottages, a lorry-load of tomatoes had been overturned in the road, and half the population had rushed to gather up this red pulp. The washing hanging before the windows of the houses flapped in the wind.

I continued along a pinewood, past the Spanish castle, to the point where our group of factory buildings becomes visible on the hillside in a graceful composition of simple planes.

Two men were waiting by the wall, and six under the covered way, where Bellomo keeps them until I arrive. I drove quickly up the drive so that they could not try to stop me, took the lift and entered my room with its terrace facing the open sea, greeting Signorina S. as I passed her table.

I had to look through five files containing a thousand applications from mechanics: we were in need of three, but the whole personnel office was in search of this handful of skilled men. I extracted the applications that seemed likeliest: the cleanest, the best-written, the fullest. It was a question of divination more than anything else. I held a letter in my hand, a man's fate, before restoring it to the files or retaining it for further consideration. Of these I made a heap on my table, but it became too big. I looked through it again: hand-writing, age, previous experience; intuition, sympathy, chance. One by one I eliminated: counting on my own experience to show me, behind the piece of paper, the face of a man.

When I had finished, I replaced the files in the cupboard. In the Signorina's room a man was waiting, Raffaele Venezia. This Venezia had been unable to explain during his interview how it was that, a native of Santa Maria, his name had so Venetian a ring; but he was possessed of excellent manual co-ordination, mechanical knowledge and a liking for mathematics. If his health held—he was wretchedly thin, and hollow-eyed—he seemed cut out to be a good worker. Actually, he passed his medical examination yesterday, which meant that he would one day be given a job.

He was already here. Consumed by the urge to work, he wanted to start immediately. The Signorina had already explained to him that as soon as we had a place we would take him on: in a week's time, maybe, or in a year.

He was standing in a corner, his eyes sunken, both fear and feigned resignation depicted on his face, while the Signorina continued her work, wondering how long he would stick it out. He stayed there almost unobserved. I spoke to the Signorina as though he were not present; but to him, it was enough not to be sent away. When I had finished speaking to her, she returned to typing the unending polite letters of refusal to the recommendations of the Bishop, the Prefect or the Mayor. Venezia drew near her again: with the voice of one begging for a drug, and without looking towards me, he again slipped in a plea that he must have work at once. The Signorina did not shout at him; indeed, while still hammering away at her typewriter, she leant her head towards him, listening to what he said, patient and perplexed. In a low voice, Venezia again insisted. "No," said the Signorina, "no, not today. Not even in a week. I can't say when. When we want you we'll send for you." Venezia went on murmuring between the typewriter and his corner. The Signorina turned to him, removing her tired arms from the typewriter and rubbing her wrists: "You have passed your medical interview. That means that you have every chance of being engaged. But not today. I've already told you that. What makes you think that if you pass your medical interview you get taken on at once? Who promised you that? We never guarantee work to anybody. Go and tell your friends that this idea about the medical interview is one you've invented yourselves. We don't try to deceive people."

Venezia retreated silently into his corner again before the Signorina's unequivocal words, but his dark eyes were unwavering. He did not go. The telephone sounded on the Signorina's desk, and from her tone of voice I knew that the Manager was speaking to her. Venezia, without understanding, listened with one ear. There was a silence, while a lengthy explanation was delivered by the Manager. In the end, Signorina S., in her dry, curt way, said: "There's a man here, one of those who passed their medical interviews yesterday." Silence again. Then: "It's Raffaele Venezia. I have told him not to come back for at least a week." Silence. "Yes, qualified for work on the assembly lines." Again the Signorina was silent: having stuck the receiver between her shoulder and her cheek she was hurriedly turning over the papers in a drawer of her desk. "No, he hasn't brought them yet . . . But how can we? At once?"

"It means that I must have the documents not later than tomorrow; tomorrow without fail . . ." The Manager's voice buzzed weakly in the receiver and Venezia and I heard it. The Signorina, resigned but flustered, gasped: "This afternoon? At two o'clock?" The Manager continued to explain; the Signorina seemed rattled, and Venezia leant forward. "This morning?" she asked, almost wearily, and then repeated: "This morning? I'll send him to the store-room, then, and have him given a working overall. I'll tell Postiglione to assign him to the assembly lines. As from when?" The Manager's voice came and went. In the meantime Venezia stared at me for a moment; then, after a short step forward, he stood poised, rigid, as though on the brink of a precipice.

"Very well," said the Signorina, putting down the receiver, and raising her head with a jerk.

"Venezia, you haven't yet got your worker's identity card. You must bring it to me tomorrow morning, with all the other documents. If you don't, you can't remain here another minute. We should have no end of trouble. A worker is now urgently needed at the assembly lines." Venezia, still rigid, could not breathe. "I am giving you this note, now go to the store and get an overall."

"I'm to go at once?"

"Yes, you're being taken on at once." His eyes flickered, not knowing on what to rest, but his olive-hued face seemed illumined. His lips were drawn back in a grimace, between laughing and crying; he could not speak, but the tears in his eyes shone, and seemed to throw a ray of light round the room and over us as well. A ray that stayed to warm our hearts.

It was the hour when the men waiting at the gates were brought in for interviewing. We see them in the laboratory now, although it puts us rather on show: from the slowly passing carts on the roadway the drivers can stare in at us, and the roar of lorries drowns our talk. But I can no longer see the applicants in my office on the managerial floor, because they sometimes, on leaving me, make a dash through the secretarial office in an attempt to reach the Manager's door. The personnel office was becoming unusable.

One passes through the middle of the building by way of the assembly-lines, the iron staircase and the workshops; then the portico and the passages connecting the dining-hall, kitchens, library and cloak-rooms. This group of social service units, in separate but communicating pavilions, with their low roofs, their walls set at different angles and coloured pale yellow, blue or pink, connects the left arm of the cross with the row of buildings along the high road. One walks along the sweet-smelling mown lawn of the garden and the ornamental pool. Since the sun is now only too hot, one seeks the shade.

The assembly-lines have become as familiar to me as a school. If, on opening the glass door of the office wing, one does not hear music being played at full blast, one hears a light purring sound from the machinery. The lines of benches stretch almost as far as one can see, with the men's heads, side by side, as in a class-room. There is still plenty of empty space, but it will gradually be filled up. Coming from the offices, one follows the production process in reverse, since it begins at the opposite end. At this one the little calculators are ready in their cases, for despatch. Then one sees them being packed. Then one passes the girls who test them when finished, and then the running-in, the checking over, and the earlier stages when they are bare, like skeletons, without their chassis. Going back along the lines, they appear more and more elementary in their forms, possessed of fewer bones, muscles and internal organs; until one reaches the original cast-iron frame-work without any organs at all. On these, the calculators are created, stage by stage, until they are put into their boxes, ready for sale. For they have to be sold; a fact not always remembered here.

The great room, overlooking the sea and the hills, its long lateral walls of glass shaded by umbrella pines, is full of a confused din that is more human in origin than mechanical.

At first sight, the work seems that of craftsmen, carried out without machinery, a work of hand and brain that each man does on his own account. But from close to, one becomes aware of the rhythm, too rapid for a craftsman, that controls the work like a set beat in a melody. The movements each man makes always take the same time, and the task of each is limited by the stage, which lasts for three minutes. The conveyor belt moves slowly amidst the men, giving them the time required: they lift the calculator from it, at shoulder-level, fit their parts into it, and pass it on, again on the conveyor, to the next man. No sooner do their hands touch it than they start their allotted task: a touch, a shake, a look inside, and then off it goes, as they hurriedly grasp another on its way. Yet this is not strictly a chain; between one line and the next, a group of waiting machines allows some margin, a breathing-space: the worker can increase his speed or slow down, decreasing or increasing this group, without affecting work on the conveyor. Some sociologists have written that it would be advisable to enlarge each man's scope, and to reunite the particles, so to speak, of mass-production work, which has broken up the process of making a given object into fragmentary stages. But here, for the present, production increases as each stage is shortened, and this is the rule we work by.

From the first landing on the iron staircase one can look down on the great cross-shaped space of the workshop. A gallery runs round it from which one can survey the whole place, with its insistent roar of machinery and the strident clash of the machines that cut out the tools, dominated always by the heavy beat of the great press.

Even in this humane workshop, the machinery is more important than the men; the men are hidden by the machines, so closely attached to them that one has to seek them out. When one passes behind them they have no time to turn round. The machinery, spurting out oil, keeps one off, and makes one's voice inaudible. But from behind one of the drills I can see the ex-fisherman, Vincenzo Palumbo, of Grotte, whose place is last on the line, near the glass wall and just by a french window that is open on to the lawn of the garden. With one step he can be out on the grass, under the open sky.

When the President of this company came down from the north to open the factory, he spoke to the workers from the corner of this gallery, above the crowd of people gathered in the centre of the workshop, with the machines at a standstill. If I were to lean over now, none of the men, their heads bent over their work, would look up from any point in the four arms of the cross; but on that day there was complete silence and attention. Speaking quickly, the President said in his cool, quiet voice: "And so, in sight of the most remarkable bay in the world, this factory has arisen. The architect's aim has been to build it in harmony with the beauty of the place, in order that, in your daily work, this beauty should be a comfort to you." No one smiled at his words.

The speaker was undemonstrative in his manner and spoke evenly, as though reading: "We wanted the life of the factory to be in touch with Nature. There was a danger that, in building too big an edifice, with enclosing walls, artificial light and air-conditioning, Nature would be shut out; so that day by day the men who entered it, however full of hope, would be changed into different beings from those they had been before."

However full of hope. The words fell on the ears of the Manager, of Di Meo, Ripamonti, and Straniero; on those of every worker in the place, from the capable, bushy-haired charge-hand at the assembly-lines to the scatterbrained worker at the running-in, who had not yet been sent downstairs, and to young Bonocore.

"The factory was therefore conceived in scale with man . . ." continued the President in his almost toneless voice, "so that he might find in his regular place of work a means of redemption and not an instrument of suffering. For this reason we have windows down to the ground and open courtyards, and a garden with trees in it, to exclude any idea of a hostile prison-like atmosphere."

Still calmly, he went on: ". . . I must mention the beautiful city of Santa Maria and its unparalleled surroundings . . ." The men from Naples looked momentarily affronted. He continued to expound his reasoning, which was wholly his own, borrowed from no one: with no intention of blandishing his hearers by high-sounding phrases. "Mankind, in being torn from the land and from contact with Nature by the machine age, has suffered in the very depths of his soul, and we cannot tell what cruel scars, what painful wounds, what irreparable injuries remain in the secret layers of his unconscious self."

To Ripamonti, who was full of pride that day, and for all his Lombard blood, greatly moved, I whispered that the man on the balcony was the only President of a great company and one of the very few engineers in Italy who gave a thought to Nature and the unconscious. Ripamonti nodded with pleasure.

"In little more than a generation we have broken up a social order that for more than a thousand years has consisted of peasants and fishermen. To this social order, which is still present in the south, God was important; the family, friends, relations and neighbours were important; the trees, the sun, the earth, the sea and the stars, were important."

Probably he had no idea how much they were in awe of him, these workers, and at the same time how greatly they needed to have faith in him: to know that he was different from the world he stood for— the world where only profits mattered, and in which there was no place for the unconscious and the stars.

When I reached the gates on my way to the laboratory, Bellomo's face was once again pale with fright. One of the labourers who had worked on the building of the factory, but who had not been taken on by us when its construction was completed, had thrown himself against the Manager's car half an hour ago. This was why the gates were so clear of waiting applicants. These incidents keep them away for a time.

They had, however, only been removed beyond the drive. There were five of them, some seated, some leaning, on the wall under the pines, indolently defying punishment. At the arrival of the "phizzico-logist" they did not react in any way, so far as one could tell from a distance. Bellomo and a second guard kept control, though somewhat shakily, over the private territory of the covered way. Bellomo asked gravely whether I wanted their cards, which I took, and went on towards the laboratory. He then waved to them to cross the road, and handed them at once over to a guard who was to see that they behaved themselves while waiting in the corridor leading to the laboratory.

The first was an old woman. She had been hiding behind a column and slipped out at the last moment. She called down blessings on me, weeping, when I received her; and naturally she had not come for herself but for her son. "Then why not send your son to me?" How-ever, nothing that I said had any effect on her; blessings and tears had drawn a veil between her and the world: she could only declare that everything depended on my kind heart and that if her son were not taken on, it was my fault. The interview must have lasted half an hour. Someone was watching us from the road, and I had to call a guard to remove him: perhaps it was the son. I drew down the Venetian blinds and the room became plunged into semi-darkness; a semi-darkness in which the old mother, fat, red-faced and dressed in black, continued to weep in comfort. She was gently led away.

The faces of those who followed were all known to me. They had come back for the second or third time. This is not allowed, and they knew it. But they try. They had already seen me at the gates.

It is hard to have a completely clear conscience. The first meeting serves for explaining, and repeating *No*: in order that the refusal may come from the lips of a man and not only from the avalanche of negative letters, all alike, that we pour every day into Santa Maria. But sometimes we become interested in those who present themselves after receiving letters of refusal. Without giving them cause to hope, a note is made of their names, and they may be summoned for the examinations; if they get through these, their names go on to the list for engagement.

They are suspicious of this manœuvre, but we cannot let the best slip through our fingers. The interview is the fine sieve that does not reject indiscriminately and that always in some way selects. The trouble is that this choice of men has necessarily to be entrusted to a man, like themselves. Is there blame in the possibility of choosing and in the impossibility, too, of establishing a scale according to individual needs, in the face of these men who have no choice? Our efforts to follow the dictates of both reason and justice are continually frustrated.

It was in this way that I came to receive two of them three times.

But Antonio Donnarumma, who came last of all, some time after mid-day, had not been before. I was writing my notes on the preceding interview when I found Donnarumma already there, with his stomach against my table. He wore a woollen pullover on his broad chest, and his grey hair stood up *en brosse*; he had a hard look in his eyes, but did not let them rest on me or the room. He simply said in a decided way: "I have got to work, Doctor."

His name was not on our files.

"Donnarumma, have you applied? When did you send in your application?"

"What application?"

"What do you mean? Don't you know that you have to write to us asking for work?"

"I don't know anything about applications. I know that I have to work, not make applications. One comes here for work, not to write letters."

"But first you must send us your application by post. We will consider it and send you an answer. How can we send you an answer if you haven't written to us?"

"And what must I write you?"

"Your application."

Unreasonable and obstinate, his eyes clouded.

"I come here and instead of giving me work you ask for this application."

"You are the first," I said quietly, "the first of thousands of people to ask for work without first applying by letter. Send your application by post, and then we'll see . . ."

"Eh, what shall we see?"

"We'll see what you tell us in your application."

"It will tell you that I must have work," he retorted, his stolid face unchanging.

"You alone must have work in the whole of Santa Maria? Do you know that forty thousand people want to come and work here?" For the first time the psychologist had left his chair. I reflected a moment and then thumped the table with my fist.

His face was pale with anger and his expression stony, like that of a deaf man; his eyes dark, red-rimmed. Grimly he raised his arm and said: "Doctor, you'd better not bang the table."

"I banged the table because you are determined not to understand. You don't want to understand, you think you have a greater claim than others, but why . . .?"

"You'd better not go on banging the table. If you do, I'll bang it myself." He raised his arm threateningly: "And it won't just be the table, but your head that will get banged. And the Manager's."

Although I had drawn up the blinds in order not to remain in the dark, I could see no one about outside. But it was not a case of calling for the guard or seizing the telephone. He continued to shout that I had better not bang the table, or he'd see that I'd never be able to do so any more.

With a firm voice I quietly replied: "I do as I think best. And you, instead of applying, want to use your fists on me and the Manager. A good way to get yourself taken on here . . ." He scowled all the more. "I don't understand why you won't write this letter . . ." He started all over again: "If I write it and send it this evening, will you send for me tomorrow? I must have work at once. But you'll tear it up like all the letters of those who want to work here."

"We don't tear them up. We consider them."

"You don't consider any of them. You bang the table and the Manager . . ."

"The Manager?"

"The Manager will have to deal with me."

"Think it over," I concluded.

He went out quickly, without turning back, even when I added:

"You are hardly putting yourself in a good light for being engaged to work here."

I shut the door at once and collected all the reports. The Manager received me immediately, behind two ash-trays heaped with cigarettes, hardly smoked beyond the tips. Pale after his second escape from an accident at the gates, he appeared calm and indifferent, leaving me to speak first.

"Those men down at the lodge . . ."

"Well, what are they doing?"

"One of them is threatening us."

"In what way?"

"He threatens to assault us."

"What is his name?"

"Donnarumma. He wants to be engaged without sending in an application." He noted the name on a card. "Christian name?" "Antonio." He put out his hand to the telephone. "I'll warn the police. Are you sure you have the name right?"

"The name is right . . . But, just a moment . . . We'll have to organize things better, they mustn't be let in. Excuse me . . . Let's wait. Don't let us call in the police."

"You don't want the police?" he said, withdrawing his arm and raising his head to look searchingly at me. "You don't want them called in?" He was ready to leave the responsibility, and with it, freedom of decision, to me.

I had to conquer fear of Donnarumma, but also the fear of defying him with a policeman at the door because we had asked for help.

"I beg you not to call in the police."

"Well, you must organize things better, then. Is it fair on the drivers of our cars to be exposed to these dangers, every day? You understand, we must be fair to all concerned; in other words, we must be firm."

CHAPTER X

THERE IS TROUBLE in the factory. The number of workers has been increased, but at the same time production has gone up by five machines per hour. The men belonging to Rubino's working group, and he, too, the best of our southern charge-hands—a studious young man with a great love for mechanical work who is inventing a new kind of lathe in his off-time—are all up in arms. Rubino is certainly not the insubordinate type. I had therefore to go down to the workshop this evening, cautiously, in search of Rubino, as I wanted to meet one of the rebels face to face.

Rubino was busy at the lathes; work that he particularly likes, although his section does other kinds as well. The bell was sounding for closing-time and the men hurried away, while he remained alone amid the silent machinery, in the quiet of the deserted workshop. Wearing dark glasses on account of his delicate eyes, he was scrutinizing a borer.

"Rubino." He jumped. "Yes, Doctor?" "Oh, it's all right, Rubino, but I heard there was some bother about the time-intervals." He cleaned his hands on a rag, delaying his reply and smiling with a hint of suspicion.

"What are the rates? Could I see for a moment?" I asked him.

He was already less apprehensive. He turned, went to the centre of the workshop, and stopped beside a drill. Putting his hand on the empty seat, and pointing to it as if the man were there, he said gravely: "This one can't get up to fifty-five per cent."

"Ah."

"The rate was fixed by our headquarters. The machine and the working of it are the same."

"Has the supervisor checked it?"

"With the time-keeper they got up to eighty," replied Rubino impassively.

"For . . . how long?"

"For . . . for ten minutes." He was still standing with his hand on the drill.

"It's rather too close, then?"

"A bit close, Doctor." Perplexed, we looked at one another.

"What does the engineer say?" The rates are a matter for the engineers, and the personnel office can only interfere exceptionally, and then only if called in for consultation.

"They are going to check up again tomorrow."

"Ah, then . . ." They must be uncertain themselves.

"How is this worker doing?"

"He's very good." This time Rubino replied with full confidence. "Only, he complains at earning too little. At first, at the presses, he earned a lot."

"Could there be anything wrong with him . . .?"

"What could have happened to him, Doctor, in three days?"

We were now alone in the workshop, with no sign of an engineer or a supervisor in the vicinity. Rubino reflected.

"I'll try it out myself, Doctor," he said. "You time it with your watch."

He climbed into the seat, as I undid my wrist-watch. With his left hand he collected some parts to be completed and with the right he grasped the lever. Then: "Go," he said, and started the machine. I stared at the second-hand of my watch, trying desperately to keep time with him. But Rubino was out of practice, and made a false start. Finally, while I kept my eyes glued to my watch, he got into his stride, lowering the lever, boring, raising it; lowering, boring, raising it. After a minute, we stopped. On working out our speed we found it came to eighty per cent.

I cannot claim to be a time-keeper, and after all, on a wrist-watch . . . But then, Rubino himself was not in practice. He began to have misgivings.

"You try, Doctor. I'll time you."

"But Rubino . . ."

"Try, Doctor, try . . ."

I climbed on to the seat. A tall man in working overalls threw open the door at the end, the one leading to the entrance hall. It was the Lombard supervisor. I seized my watch from Rubino and got down. We abandoned the drill and quietly, assuming an indifferent air, made our way out as quickly as possible, as though we were a couple of thieves.

Monday

Still no application from Donnarumma; I look through the post every morning in the hopes of seeing a letter from him.

This morning he was in the group at the entrance, looking

indifferent, but clearly in a black humour. Beside him there were Accettura, Chiodo with his boy, and Conte; then Dattilo and the old woman whom I had already interviewed. Further off stood three or four new ones.

They made way for my car, though Donnarumma drew back reluctantly. I would have passed quickly through the gates if Bellomo had not wanted to hand a report in at my window. They gathered round as I stopped, but Bellomo pretended to ignore them.

I started in low gear to move off, looking straight ahead. Someone would now throw himself under the car: that would be the result of refusing to have the police on the spot. I saw Donnarumma's head go by my windows, but it seemed that his thoughts were elsewhere, and as I passed Conte, tall and pale, he gave me a bow. The old woman was weeping, her handkerchief in her hand; Dattilo stood apart, against the gate, invoking my attention with his eyes alone.

My radiator was just at the open gate when Chiodo shoved his son, a slip of a boy, all eyes, towards me. For a moment I thought he would go under my mudguard. The boy almost pitched forward, then straightened himself. His father had not the courage to give him another push.

Chiodo now always has this boy with him. Having been employed on the building of the factory he is now one of those who claim that they have a right to work within the walls raised by the sweat of their brows. But illiterate building labourers are of no use for light mechanical work.

Last week he waylaid the Manager three times at the door of his house in the city: and on Wednesday he tried to throw himself under his car.

On Thursday, Chiodo was told that he was over the age limit for a job in the factory, and was asked if he had a son. On Saturday he brought the boy with him, a puny little fifteen-year-old, more feeble even than Ugo, with a small head and arms like a doll's.

"Chiodo, haven't you got a bigger boy?" The child was standing at his side, listening.

"This is the eldest. Didn't you want the eldest? The others are fourteen, eleven, nine, seven, and five years old. Then there are two girls."

"He is rather . . . young for work here. Perhaps in a few years' time." Would that time ever come?

"In a few years' time?" raged the father. "So I am too old and the boy is too young. You're laughing at me, Doctor." He was the same

build as Donnarumma, very short, with curly black hair, and as he
started to argue his eyes became bloodshot.

"We told you that we could take a son of yours instead of yourself.
But you have brought us . . . you have brought us a child," I said in a
low voice, so that the boy should not hear.

"So he's a child, is he? You won't have me, and you say he's just a
child?" He was shouting at the top of his voice. "And what do you
want then, the babies, the girls, the women?" He gesticulated wildly.
The boy looked dumbly on, and then, as the man's fury ebbed for a
moment, they were sent away and told to come back on Monday,
today.

Accettura we know already. He has not been seen about lately.
But this morning he waved to me in a friendly manner with his good
arm, his one precious possession.

Conte was interviewed a year ago by another psychologist, who
had written on his file: *neurasthenic*. As my car passed him this morning,
I had glimpsed his long, white face, as he bowed with a gentlemanly
but slightly mad air. The diffident Dattilo on the other hand had come
to see me last night at my own house, having been the first to discover it by following my wife home after she had been down to the
sea for a bathe.

We have been hastily examining a batch of applications from
skilled workers. The best of them are employed in neighbouring
factories, and we should have to take them from their jobs; many of
them come originally from the north. Even down here the firms are
competing for northerners already employed.

How can we oppose our engineers if they ask for skilled men? The
experts are always trying to speed up production, and it takes time to
train the youngsters. The personnel office has to take a broad view,
keeping its social aims in mind but also fulfilling immediate needs. If
the Signorina and I were faced by the urgent necessity for help in our
work, would we be prepared to spend a year in teaching a beginner?

The skilled mechanics of the south—especially those already in work
—are extremely good: serious and accurate, they show an engaging
eagerness, as though their unusual choice of a training that is in
opposition to local traditions has forged in them the will to succeed.
Fully-qualified mechanics are not the fashion in the south: and those
who decide to follow technical courses instead of aiming at university
degrees come to their jobs fresh from their training, and with all the
enthusiasm of a true vocation. It is in the technical experts that one

finds the southerner developing at his best, encouraged by having an outlet for the keen intelligence that has never been lacking down here, but which, throughout the centuries, has too often gone to waste.

If they are not employed by the big concerns, where we generally leave them from motives of good neighbourliness, and in order not to upset the labour market with our high wages (although if a free economy is wanted, competition in the labour market must be accepted) the trained men who come to us have mostly been in small firms, to which they have gone at once on obtaining their diplomas. With these they have no contracts and no security; they are only kept on as a favour, and are sacked at the slightest complaint. They are in fact only engaged, and paid, as ordinary workers. What, then, is the use of a diploma? And can it, therefore, be true that there is such a shortage of trained men in southern Italy?

It is a pity that the management has decided not to engage the worker Armando Barca.

The man of the south is not different from others, but he is a man deformed in his inmost being. The hazards of his life, and the history of this region, have made him such that ordinary standards cannot be applied to him. Both well-to-do and poor suffer from a sense of being out of their depth, with no hope of finding anything to which they can cling for support.

But what is to happen to Armando Barca, intelligent and quick-minded as he is, strong, and in good health?

As a young man he had been employed in a factory, doing work at the lathes, which was to be his real job. Then the factory closed. He became manager of a bar. He sold tickets in the summer at the Exhibition. Then he became a commercial traveller, and then he again worked in a bar.

At thirty-five, he wants to get back to his original work. The stuff he is made of has been so handled and mishandled, so bruised and battered, that, well, he certainly is not what he was. Who could rely on him now? In the same twenty years a man in the north would have made his way up in the same factory to become one of those steady technical experts on whom our civilization depends. But Barca . . .

From the wide window of my office I looked towards the road, a tract of which, with the pavement, is visible. It was half-past one, and I wondered whether Donnarumma was still there. Was he the man leaning against the wall? It would be easy, but cowardly, to slip out by the service entrance, near the hillside. The Signorina is amused at the idea that Donnarumma should succeed in inspiring fear.

All seemed quiet on the road. It was a quarter to two; the group at the entrance had given way to hunger and disappeared; Donnarumma in his jersey was no longer hanging about among the oleanders or leaning against the wall. The guard had gone into his cabin and the sea, flecked by a light breeze, was brilliant under the mid-day sun. The light on the road along the volcanic hillside was blinding. But when my car reached the shade of the pines, there was Accettura limping along the pavement.

Which way was he going to turn? Would he throw himself at my car, even though we were not at the usual place of encounter, the entrance to the factory? If he were to do so at this time, the two of us would be alone on the highway, face to face.

I could slow down in order not to hurt him: or I could swerve rapidly to avoid him altogether. Perhaps he would not recognize my car. But hearing its approach, he turned, and, keeping well on the pavement, signalled to me to stop.

"Doctor, will you give me a lift to Santa Maria?" Only those familiar with his peculiar speech can understand him. I opened the door for him to get in.

"I'm going home, Doctor."

"But don't you live under . . . under the road here?"

"I'm going to get something to eat."

"Where do you eat?"

"I manage somehow . . . I'm not working," he said calmly. "My wife has left me. She couldn't wait any longer."

"Ah, you're married?"

"My wife has left me because I'm out of work." He made no complaint, but stared at the road.

"Women don't understand, Doctor. They have no patience . . ."

"We have to have patience, too, Accettura . . ."

"It's true. Women can't wait a day. My mother is dead, so I'm alone. But nothing matters to me but work." He was sitting calmly on the edge of the seat, his useless arm hanging down, and with the other hand clutching the door-handle: staring ahead to see where he was being taken, almost as though he thought he had been kidnapped. Where had he been all this time? He was muttering away, his language more incomprehensible than ever.

"What did you say, Accettura?"

He thought a moment. "Nothing matters to me but work and food, Doctor. Hunger's bad."

"Yes, I know, Accettura."

We skirted the Roman amphitheatre, and reached the lane up to San Rocco. Accettura was still in his corner, hanging like a spider from the door-handle. Would he refuse to get out?

"Work and food, Doctor," he said, thinking aloud. "Work and food." The two words rang clear.

"Thank you, Doctor."

I opened the door and he slipped out like a well-mannered passenger, without another word.

Tuesday

Word has already gone round that the head of the personnel office has given Accettura a lift in his car. The Signorina avers that I have become a friend of his.

It is the end of June; cheerful bathers from the town have invaded the iron-hued beach of Castello and the first of the middle-class holiday-makers have rented the bathing-huts at Grotte. The other evening Dattilo followed my wife on her return from the beach, with her wet bathing-costume in her hand, as far as our garden, but left her when she entered the house. Then he rang the door-bell: she went on to the balcony above the entrance and looked over, thinking it was a visitor.

Dattilo began to speak quietly, in his gentle, persuasive way, his head raised towards the balcony. He had had no recommendations, either from bishops or ministers: why was he the only one not allowed to do the examinations, why was I against him, why did I persecute him? It was not a heated protest. He just wanted to arouse pity.

My wife could hardly hear what he was saying. But the thought struck her that the young man might be the first victim of the sterner measures introduced after Donnarumma's threats, and she did not at at once go back into the house.

"I am Antonio Dattilo. May I wait for the doctor?"

"My husband is not allowed to see applicants at home. It's not advisable, for either of you . . . Go and see him at his office, otherwise he'll be angry. It's a better way for you, too."

"Better for me, Signora!" Dattilo smiled suddenly, letting his sad eyes rest on the garden. "There is no better way for me." She made a move to withdraw.

Dattilo said, in a sudden outburst: "It's hell for me, Signora, if I'm not in work."

"Are you one of a big family . . .?" she asked.

"A family . . . it's worse than belonging to a family. If I don't work I don't eat, and I lose the light of reason, I lose heart . . ." said Dattilo softly, insidious but touching, as he drew nearer to the great carob-tree that rustles against our window-panes.

"You must have faith. Go and see him tomorrow at the office."

"No, no, he won't receive me. I'm the only one he won't see."

"Of course it's not only you. He can't see everyone. He's kind, but how could he possibly do so? Do you think he has an easy job?"

Leaving the tree, Dattilo approached the house and, leaning against the wall, for once dropped his shyness altogether and declared in a loud voice: "Even he is not in Paradise! We are in hell and he is in Purgatory. But he is nearer Paradise than we are. Your husband is not just kind, he is too kind. I know it, Signora. He will get to Paradise before us."

"Well, no. No, no. But he is certainly over-worked; you can't imagine how heavy his work is; he would like to content you all, but he simply cannot. You who haven't work . . . you can't make comparisons."

"He's worse off than me, your husband," Dattilo insisted with a wave of the hand. "Yes, he is," and he glanced timidly along the road down which the husband would soon be coming. "But I am different from the rest, Signora," he sighed, looking up at her with his sad, childlike eyes. "You don't know about me."

"Why do you think yourself different from the others?" He seemed to find comfort as he listened to her, and she went on: "Everyone has great need of work here, everyone. It is the old problem of your beautiful but unfortunate land . . . it's been going on for centuries. The factory helps, but it can't wipe out history at one blow . . ." She regretted not having used a simpler phrase; in search of one, she paused, and was interrupted.

"No one is in my position, Signora. I'm married . . . But not by the Church."

"Aren't you a Catholic?" she asked, leaning over the balustrade, her interest caught by this one non-Catholic in the district. It was at this moment that Dattilo let her see right into his mind: "An unemployed man is not a Catholic. An unemployed man cannot be blessed." It was she, now, who did not understand.

"My wife, the girl I'm engaged to," said Dattilo, "has been turned out of her home by her father. Before that, I lived at home and she lived with her parents. I used to visit her there, while we waited for the priest's blessing. We'll marry when I have work, when we have a room. Her father turned her out. And then where was she to go? I took her to my home, and my mother lets her share her bed."

"And you sleep . . . where?"

"At home."

"With your mother? Are you with your wife . . . your . . ."

"Under the same roof, but in separate rooms," he reassured her with dignity, raising a hand as though to ward off all thought of an accusation. Then, humiliated, he said with an audible sigh: "You understand, Signora."

"You are . . . married?"

"Married? Engaged."

"Yes, but you will marry? This civil marriage . . . or, afterwards, a church ceremony?"

"When God wills, Signora."

"And when will God will it?" He raised his eyes to her, subtly playing on her sympathy; and held out his arms. "You understand me, Signora. My nerves. Adjoining rooms. The girl sleeps with my mother, we have lived for three months beneath the same roof. She, too, is worn out, overwrought. Rooms next door to one another, in the summer. It is she who has sent me here. She has to wait till they take me on at your husband's factory, she has to wait, wait . . . who can hold out, in the summer?"

She stared at him: thin and wasted, sleepless with nervous strain, tied by civil bonds to a woman, but without the priest's blessing that would have united them; what sort of a tangle was this? Dattilo seemed consumed with love.

She disappeared into the house the moment my car came round the corner. Dattilo drew near the tree to take cover.

"No, no, not here," I exclaimed, as I got out of the car and banged the door. "If you come here, you lose all hope of getting a job with us." It was only by frightening him that I could make him leave. Instead he murmured to me from a few paces away:

"I have dared to speak to your wife. My situation is different from the others. Your wife has been so kind. If only you, too, would listen to me, Doctor . . . It's my nerves, in this summer weather. My wife and I sleep in rooms next door to one another."

"No, no, not here, Dattilo. Not here!" It was an impossible situation and he had to be sent away. He began slowly to leave the garden, turning now and again, as though expecting some miracle.

"It's for this that I'm in the office, Dattilo, just for this! If you come here you'll lose any hope you have of being accepted!"

Refusing to give way to temptation, I entered the house. My wife was watching him from a window on the first floor.

Highly strung—even a year ago, before his civil marriage—responsive but confused in his mind, Dattilo had been rejected after his tests by my predecessor at the factory: if an exception were to be made in his case, one would have to call back all those refused for similar reasons. He was bright enough, but feckless, a leaf blown by the wind; what job could we expect to settle him at, in the workshops?

"What is he doing, what is he doing now?" asked my wife, still trying to see him through the window.

"He's going away."

The table was laid: with the shutters pulled to, to shield us from the dazzling glare from the sea, we sat down to eat. I told her that there were many in Dattilo's situation, married only before the civil authorities. The girls have no faith in an engagement; if there is no bed for them in which to sleep with a husband, they want to marry at the Municipality in order to hold these unemployed men to their word, anyway before the law. I had interviewed at least a dozen placed like Dattilo. As to when they are really to consummate their marriages, that remains a mystery.

After we had eaten, I picked up the newspaper and read: "At midnight this evening the 1,200 employees at the Castello cement works are beginning the fifth day of their vigorous fight in defence of their rights as free men and for the application in full of the new agreement on conditions of work in the cement industry." The fifth day of their vigorous fight? We had heard nothing about it.

CHAPTER XI

Wednesday

Oᴜʀ ᴏᴡɴ ᴄʟᴇᴀɴ factory, with its light mechanical products has never had any contact with the cement works at Castello, which exist as though in another world, primitive and dirty; it is not that we despise them but because we live here in a certain isolation. Even Straniero was ignorant of the strike; Castello is divided from Santa Maria by three kilometres, a desert of prickly pears and stunted pines. The cement workers in Italy had won a new national agreement on terms of work in the industry, but the cement company at Castello—with the greater part of its capital in Danish hands—had withdrawn from the Association of employers, in order not to sign it: why should they sign an Italian collective agreement just because they had opened a factory in southern Italy?

At seven in the evening, coming up from the lower road and rounding the corner of the steel-works, I found the premises of the Communist headquarters closed; only the dark doorway of the Socialist Club was wide open, showing the usual card-players at their tables. A group of men who looked like workers, although down here they are never stamped unmistakably so, like the northern proletariate, were standing about on the pavement near the newspaper kiosk. I thought that they would be discussing the action of the cement-workers, on the other side of the wall from the steel-works; but a young city intellectual or middle-class inhabitant of Castello was enlightening them on the subject of neo-realism in the cinema as the only true popular art. This corner, formed by the dark walls of the steel-works, is the most advanced point of the southern workers' organization, even though its scope is restricted in extent.

But the "vigorous fight" at the cement works, a hundred yards away and already of five days' duration, had not apparently reached even so far as this.

Continuing to the left of the steel-works, one skirts an impenetrable wall that shields two factory chimneys and a large furnace from view and then ends in a lifeless quarter of shabby buildings and empty streets. Children play in the dusty roadway. The once showy houses, battered by past bombardments, formerly belonged to higher officials of the steel-works, who, transferred from the north, had tried to reproduce in them the pretensions of modern civilization; but they are now in-habited by working-class families, and the quarter ends only in a space full of rubbish along the wall of the factory.

I turned back, and passing beneath the railway bridge took the main road that runs below the long bastion of the cape, as far as the steep, wooded point itself.

Eucalyptus trees and other greenery shade the gates and lawns at the entrance to the cement works, and combine, with its nineteenth-century façade, to give the effect of a bathing establishment rather than a factory.

A dense group of men had gathered here, against the gates, while behind them a number of women and workers, some lying on the grass or eating peacefully, crowded the piazza.

The gates were barred. A notice hung from them: "The present strike is injurious to output. Any worker wishing to enter the factory must sign an undertaking to work the full eight hours of the shift." In fact, they were striking by fits and starts.

"They haven't got their cards. The management has withdrawn them," an old man informed me.

"How do you get in, then?"

"You can't get in."

"Is nobody inside?"

"The works committee is with the assistant manager. The Manager is at his own house. He says he won't leave it. The men for this shift are here, outside." They were the group at the gates. The others, walking about or eating their sandwiches, belonged to other shifts: they were adhering to the normal practice of one shift at work and two off, but they were carrying it out in front of the works. It was already a lockout.

Thursday

A day later, and still the same spectacle at the cement works: a group of men pressed against the gates and others, with many women, in the piazza.

However, the workers of one shift had succeeded in entering the plant, and now they could not leave it. Their relatives, with bags and baskets, were bringing the prisoners their supper.

One of the heads, a Dane, was expected at the works.

With one whole shift shut up in the factory, the situation comprised, at the same time, a strike, a lockout and occupation of the factory by the workers, with ramifications as far away as Denmark: and thus called for intervention by the city trade-union leaders, who were now addressing the workers.

One of them, Di Nonno, a former metallurgical worker and now secretary of the Workers' Club, was arguing with some of the women. A fine-looking man, taller than the rest and with smooth black hair, he was exerting his charm on all around him. He led the women into the shade of some eucalyptus trees behind a hedge to plot in secret with them; the women workers, always an uncertain element, can often prove the success or failure of a strike. Then he returned without them, and seizing upon an indolent labourer in a sleeveless vest, got him to take a message; ran to another, but turned suddenly back again, as though he had been called. He was the only one who seemed in a cheerful frame of mind.

The men standing around appeared calm and confident; too calm and confident. If a works committee is united, a strike on working conditions will show a solid front. For the time being, since they were united, this was enough for them and they believed in their strength. But Di Nonno was worried; he was putting out feelers and seemed to fear coming trouble.

Saturday

July is on us, and the heat is intense. With it, even our own fine factory is showing signs of subversive activity. We do not all know as yet the demands put forward by our shop stewards, since the rank and file are restless, but uninformed; but there are demands in plenty. At two this afternoon the Manager came out from a meeting with the workers' representatives, his jacket soaked with perspiration, as though a pail of water had been thrown over him.

Yesterday, after some days, there seemed nothing new at the cement works, except the appearance of the police. Two heavy jeeps stood beside the gates. The workers inside were still there, supplied with food in baskets, saucepans, or tied up in handkerchiefs. The piazza looked so unchanged that one might have thought the people gathered at the barriers and those passing the time behind them were the same as before. But they were, in fact, taking turns at being there.

Di Nonno was no longer on his own; he was walking up and down on the roadway with a short, bespectacled official who had been sent down from Rome for consultation, and was listening respectfully to him.

It seemed that the workers felt no need for decisions, but were content to stay there passively; they made no plans for the future—indeed, they had no plan of campaign at all.

The old man to whom I had spoken on Wednesday was not a cement-worker himself, but an artisan. He had a daughter who was trapped inside with the others. Yesterday they brought her supper to her again, and today he was still there, with his bicycle, waiting with the rest, near where I was standing. But suddenly Di Nonno came up to him and said: "Get her out, send for her. Take her home. They're minors."

The old man, too, did not want his daughter to spend another night there, sleeping in the workshops, where the men and women were mixed together. Glad of Di Nonno's moral authority he made his way to the gates.

During the day, delegations from those inside were keeping contact with their comrades on the piazza, and exchanging the food baskets. The old man parleyed with one of these, then returned. As Di Nonno had already hurried away, he leaned on the handlebars of his bicycle and said to me: "One can't work with strikes. One can't eat."

The gate opened. A young girl, dirty and unkempt, and wearing a black apron, came running out. Her father, still standing beside me, seemed to derive confidence from my presence, and did not move towards her.

"I'm not going home with you," panted the girl, as she grasped the handlebars of his bicycle.

"You must come out. Your mother wants you at home. What are you doing in there?" he said, with the thin, nasal drawl of the people here. But just as he had already shaken his head over the question of strikes, so he now seemed uncertain, sceptical.

"The others aren't coming out. I won't come alone. I'm staying."

"The secretary says you should leave. You must sleep at home tonight. A girl like you . . ."

"Father, I'm not coming, do you understand?" Petulant, excited, her little face flushed and grubby, his daughter defied him; she only wanted to rush back to the factory. "Do you understand?" He was still uncertain, possibly even a little afraid of her. But now perhaps he would give her a smack in the face to make her obey.

These seventeen-year-olds, with their childish heroism, seemed to be enthusiastic supporters of the occupation: the little slut appeared more decided than ever, and the old man was at a loss to know how to deal with her.

"Signorina," I begged her, "the Secretary of the union thinks you

D

should not remain inside . . ." She looked only at her father and said: "We'll come out when the police fire on us."

Her father said, firmly, as he took her by the arm: "You're not to spend another night here. Your mother has your bed ready for you. I'm going to take you home." The girl was frantic to return, and thrilled by the adventure of this occupation of the factory. Evidently it was the youngest who were most daring, standing together like a bulwark against the tyranny of their foreign masters.

Even the old artisan, her father, seemed troubled, for the first time, by this struggle on the part of workers and young girls together.

"Father, the others are not leaving. I can't come alone. The others are staying, Father, you can't take me away." It was clear that she was not going to betray her companions. Yet, although almost defeated, the old man might still work up one of those southern explosions of wrath, of blind, sexual pride in the honour of a girl of his family. He began to mutter, and looked round for Di Nonno.

The latter, some way away, was walking up and down the road beside the city intellectual, bending his raven-haired head the better to take in the other's words of wisdom. The old man hesitated in embarrassment, and seeing him uncertain, the girl let go of his bicycle and sped away, disappearing into the works. He was not greatly surprised and went on waiting, leaning on his bicycle.

"She's courageous, your daughter. How could you send her home?" I said to him, more moved by the incident than he was.

"She and I are the only ones in work. There are four other children and my wife to support." He did not seem much upset.

"Is she the eldest?"

"Yes. Luckily she's been working here for a year."

"Certainly, it's unfortunate . . ."

"If she comes out now, they'll take on another, and she'll lose her job. That's why the women are staying. If they come away, the management will engage others who are unemployed."

"No, no, surely not," I exclaimed. So that was why the women would not leave.

Di Nonno returned. He looked quickly round and saw that the girl was not with us.

"Where is she? Have you persuaded her? Are you taking her home?"

"She's gone back to the others," said the father. "She's gone back in there," he repeated almost defiantly.

"They're out of their minds," shouted the trade unionist for all to hear. All the same the voice with which he was accustomed to dominate his hearers sounded disheartened. "They're mad. What can they do in there? Why don't they go home?"

It seemed strange that even in an industrial struggle of the south the good name of the women should mean so much to him. He made such a point of it that the old father, shorter than Di Nonno by a head, winked at me and repeated: "If the women come out, they'll lose their jobs."

Di Nonno had turned away, leaving things as they were. He was trying to gather a more reasonable audience round him, and went again towards the eucalyptus grove, hoping to be followed there anyway by the women.

He wanted secretly to form, from the crowd of workers standing, anxious but courageous, before the gates, a group in support of some move of his own. The very resistance of the strikers was now imperilled if they did not understand that their calm, negative attitude was not helping them. By why did Di Nonno want to work in secret?

In order to reach the gates myself, I cut through the groups of men near the entrance. All respectfully made way for me, since I did so with assurance: I might be some Dane, a representative sent by the owner in Denmark—who had not yet been seen on the spot—or a secret messenger from the Manager. The latter was still shut up in his apartment in the city, with his wife and children, letting time pass and relying on the weaker side to tire first. He was not standing before barred gates, nor wondering whether he would be paid for his days off work. It was said, however, that he too had his vexations: a ship that had come from South Africa to take on board a cargo of cement was held up at anchor in the port.

With my nose close to the bars of the gate I could almost touch those of the prisoners, both voluntary and enforced. They all looked enquiringly at me. I was pushed forward. On the bars hung a notice which appeared to be that of Wednesday, signed by the management: "The present strike is injurious . . ."

"Read it," shouted a woman behind me. "It comes from the magistrates."

In fact, the notice was a new one: a legal injunction issued at the instance of the management, and ordering that the owners should recover full control of their property. Another group was now hedging me in from behind. I refrained from saying a word and turned away.

Di Nonno had tried to stop the girls sleeping on the premises not in order to preserve their virginity but because he did not want an occupation of the factory. And he wanted to avoid this because the unions were not feeling strong enough to support it against a judicial injunction and a lockout. But he felt that this weakness must be concealed from the workers, and therefore tried to convince the women, who did not understand him. The men, too, failed to understand him: they were conscious of one single fear, the fear that others, now unemployed, would joyfully come to replace them, and it was this fear that made them more courageous than if they had understood what he was driving at.

Monday

Our own workers have at last delivered their demands. They ask for their categories to be defined; for an increase in hourly rates of pay; an extension of paid holidays; a reduction in the hours of work; and a bonus on profits. According to correct trade union practice, they are attacking on every front in the hope of breaching the enemy's lines at least on one.

Yesterday, Sunday, was a holiday at the cement works. Unlike our people, they are hanging on to their one demand, and if they lose their hold they will have nothing to fall back on. On the green lawns and under the eucalyptus trees a crowd of men and women scarcely smaller than on the preceding days was still waiting. In the morning they had sent a delegation of several dozen women, workers and wives of workers, to the Prefecture, "to confer on the dispute with the representative of the Government". This custom of sending the women forward still persists down here. No sooner did they reach the piazza than they were joined by another band of shouting women who had been turned out of the poor-house and the war-damaged school-building, and had already been to the town hall to demand a roof over their heads. They all went on to the Prefecture together, feeling stronger at finding themselves shoulder to shoulder. Such great disorder resulted from this merging of the two streams that the police came out to repress it with a truly martial display of force.

As the setting sun fell on the sombre green slopes of the Cape, and the workers at the cement factory remained cut off from the usual animation of a Sunday evening in summer, it seemed that the strike was becoming more and more drawn-out and disquieting.

No further thought was given to the women's adventure of this morning. The shift that had refused to leave the factory had at last given in, the trade union leaders having insisted that women and men could not continue to sleep together on the premises. Even the old artisan's daughter had gone home, reassured that the management did not intend to replace her. Now the lockout was a real lockout, and the strikers, by renouncing occupation of the factory, could claim to be wholly within their rights.

But where does the real strength lie? The Danish director does not come; the managing-director will not receive the works committee; the South African ship is still waiting for its cargo and the management will have to pay the heavy fine that is running up for their delay in consigning it. The workers have lost their pay for the whole of last week, and their case has ended in the hands of the magistracy, the Prefecture and the Ministry. Still united, they are left to nurse their anger and their grievances.

When I drive home in the warm twilight and see again the wide stretch of sea from our terrace, the cement works, our own factory and every other factory seem very far away. A palm-tree in the garden hides part of the sea from my gaze. Solitude is here, with only the intermittent sounds of the countryside; a few lights gleam from the old, square houses; one hears a song or two, and in the remote distance the noise of the steel-works.

At night we are completely alone. Why are we here, my wife and I? Just to hear the far-away sound of the ships' hooters? Or to contemplate the moonlight on the Bay, with its fabulous islands and capes?

Friday

The organization in the north has had the initiative to send us down here, among people we know, in a land we love. Certainly these people cannot possibly guess a fraction of our cares; they know nothing of the scientific skill of our work and our historic industrial conflicts. That the industrialization of this region is an element in the problem of the south, in other words their own problem, leaves them indifferent; if anything, it makes them suspicious. The nobles denounce it. For the peasants, who at nightfall go barefoot among the vines round their houses and up the arid, terraced hillsides by paths edged with prickly pears, or who shut themselves up in the new houses on the main road, it is just a great banquet from which to pick up some crumbs for themselves: especially as the doctor who selects workers is living amongst them.

The middle-class shopkeepers and tradesmen who have built their country houses in this coastal region have other more traditional aims to pursue. With their love of speculation in building and their interest in the tourist trade, they regard industry as an enemy, to be kept at bay.

In fact, industry is isolated here, a drop in the ocean, a grain of sand, in a social order consisting of fishermen without boats and peasants without land. No bonds unite one factory with another, and there is no proletariate. Nor does unemployment unite the workers; it divides them, except when it explodes.

This morning we had tests again in the laboratory. From outside, Donnarumma watched us through the windows.

Signorina S. had suddenly caught sight of him. He had first paused on the pavement on the other side of the high-road; then he crossed over to look through the windows. Still wearing his woollen pullover, he was scowling balefully, with a most disapproving air. We let down the venetian blinds, cutting him off from view before he had a chance to distract the candidates.

The piazza in front of the cement works is empty now; the dispute has been settled. We have not heard anything about it here, but there is a somewhat obscure article in one of the morning papers from which it is hard to tell who has won. The newspapers of the Right never report such matters, and those of the Left are unwilling to reveal defeats. But it seems that the struggle has ended in a compromise: the workers have obtained application of the national agreement, but no increase in pay. Thus the old artisan and his daughter, the manual workers, Di Nonno and my friends of a week, have fought their fight for the letter of the law and for justice.

CHAPTER XII

Saturday

WE ARE SHOWING firmness towards the applicants at the entrance. We will not receive Dattilo or Chiodo, or Conte, or any of them.

The implacable July sun, with its constant glare, fills the whole horizon from early dawn. It drains both sea and landscape of colour. The moment the sun has risen the quivering air grows burning hot, and the earth of the hillside above our house turns almost white, beneath a pale sky.

Perhaps it is pleasanter in the factory, despite its glazed walls. But in any case, the works committee is now demanding paid holidays for all the girls who test the completed calculators, on the grounds that their fatigue has come to a head with the summer heat.

They are the twenty dark-complexioned women, among them one or two with fair hair, who sit in two rows at the end of the assembly-lines, on the side nearest the offices. In their white overalls, and using both arms, they work the handles of the calculating machines up and down, one to each hand. The same tests are tapped out on a continuous strip of paper; miles of twisted, numbered strips surround them, wrap them round, and slip to the ground like snakes.

The working girls in the north have always tested the machines one at a time, with one hand. Here, at the opening of the factory, a girl who already knew how to use a calculator wanted to occupy her free hand instead of leaving it in her lap, and asked to be given a second machine. Her companions followed suit, and all succeeded in manœuvring two at a time. In the early days of the factory, the prowess of the women of Santa Maria stood out as the great achievement of the southern factory.

In the time allowed for testing one machine, they did two: and they were thus earning double pay, more than that of the skilled work-men and the clerical staff. Some adjustment was obviously called for, and they agreed with the management to be paid at the rate of one and a half.

They still earn a great deal; and they are always ready to work overtime, in pursuit of a mirage of wealth that is their very own: women who, at Santa Maria, are never expected to produce money, only children. These are the richest girls in southern Italy, chained to their benches by their own hands. Who should ever tempt them away from this work?

For the last three months we have been expecting the arrival of some mechanized plant that will render them all useless; but its continued delay preserves their hopes and their unbelief. Not one of them, however, wants to go and work among the oily machines of the workshop, to wear a black overall and sit at the benches like a man, with a screwdriver. A woman of Santa Maria would regard it as dishonourable.

They continue turning out miles of paper, until they reach a state of nervous exhaustion. Working the levers of the two machines backwards and forwards with both hands, from morning to night, as though rowing, they interrupt the movement only to tap the numbers on the keyboard. They tap from memory, with the tips of their slender fingers, and then pull the lever. Tap and pull, tap and pull. Their inquisitive black eyes follow those who pass by them as they swing the handles in a single movement. They are working for their freedom, or at least for their trousseaux.

If the average standard of piece-work in the whole factory is as high as it now is, a great deal of the credit is due to these girls, and it is for this reason that the works committee has asked for a special award to them of a holiday in the mountains.

Monday

Before the summer holidays, Straniero is going to have a strike. He had said he would. A new agreement is being considered, and the works committee cannot let the political initiative escape from them; the company's headquarters in the north are preparing the great event of the reduction of working-hours without reducing wages.

After the bell had gone for the mid-day break, and indeed before, Straniero had been coming and going between the assembly-lines, the secretarial office and our rooms, so full of papers about which he knows nothing, and then back to the assembly-lines. He argues with everyone and penetrates into every corner of the works, being himself now established as an official of the opposition. In his eyes, it is a duel between the Manager and himself: his rebellion reaches as far as the writing-tables of the authorities. For that matter, in this organization, which is much more democratic than that of other firms, our psychological and humanistic functions always keep us in touch with the troubles of the workers.

He was worried, and—his shirt open halfway down his chest—

he came up to my table, but did not speak, though he had just been arguing with the Signorina. Now, in my room, he scrutinized me as a trade unionist might a representative of his employers: as though we were two enemies of long standing who, before facing one another, prowl round and sniff the air, like dogs.

He leant his elbow on the table. Then he began to explain his method of thought, which consists in putting questions to himself and facing up to them. He stopped, and lifted his elbow from the table.

"Doctor, this time I have told myself that the strike is necessary."

"When?"

"It doesn't matter when: sooner or later."

"Is it necessary for one reason only; in other words, for some particular demand, or for . . . many reasons?"

"You understand, Doctor! For many reasons!" His eyes gleamed. We both knew what the other meant: it was to be a demonstration, for reasons of prestige; but he couldn't admit that. And as an honest official, there was only one thing that I could say to him, one thing that was well within democratic limits. "Strike, but only if you are sure that you will succeed."

"We are sure."

"Because a strike that fails in this factory will be the end of strikes here altogether."

With a malicious gleam in his eye he exclaimed: "You're very shrewd, Doctor!"

Shrewd, because as an official I was suggesting a measure of trade union tactics, a programme more astute than that of a fight, or because he was letting the flame die while seeming to do his best to fan it?

"I may be shrewd, Straniero . . ." He sighed and fingered the papers on my desk, his thoughts elsewhere.

"A strike . . . because they don't believe that we . . . But we are capable of resisting to the end. Though perhaps those that have just been taken on . . ." He was questioning himself again.

"All workers, whether in the north or the south, once they have decided for themselves, are capable of supporting strike action."

"Doctor, you're a good chap, and you're shrewd!" He had regained his animation, and his blue eyes twinkled as though he had discovered a secret. "You're shrewd, but take care!" He grinned. "For me, you are always one of the management, and what you say . . . I remember what you say, and use it for my own ends . . ." The stock Machiavellian threat gave him great satisfaction; he felt himself on the edge of the class-war and at the same time in the management's councils. Walking to and fro, he stopped for a moment to let his glance rest on the archives.

"I'll remember that, Straniero!"

"Good-bye, Doctor!"

He hurried off to see the Manager. He was enjoying his own importance. However, in the afternoon he met the shadow of defeat. He experienced one of those clashes between representatives and represented that cut the earth from beneath the feet of the leaders. It was the women who let him down, though unintentionally. Why had he not made sure of them first? Or had the girls of the machine testing really deceived him?

The management, having accepted the request for a holiday in the mountains, had given the social assistant instructions to choose a hotel at a healthy, bracing altitude; and to summon the twenty girls, one by one, to inform them of their reward.

But I met the Signorina from the welfare office in the corridor, red in the face with youthful exasperation: "They won't have anything to do with it, Doctor, seventy per cent of them won't accept. They prefer to stay in Santa Maria. Their mothers won't let them . . . their young men won't let them. They're afraid. We'd have to force them. And who is to force them to go to the mountains? They all prefer the sea."

Tuesday

Donnarumma's application has never appeared in the post. Accettura, too, seems to have disappeared. But Donnarumma in the flesh, grim and resentful, spends the mornings at the entrance, together with Chiodo and his boy, Dattilo, and the neurasthenic Conte. They nod to us as we pass; or else they sit further off in the shade, on the wall.

"What on earth has become of Accettura?" I wondered aloud to the Signorina, who was opening her morning post. We were speaking from one room to the other. "Do you miss him, Doctor?" A minute later she came into my room like a gust of wind, with a letter in her hand.

"To the Manager: Sir, If you do not engage us all before the 15th of this month, there will be six bullets for you. From a desperate friend." A skull and crossbones replaced a signature.

It was impossible to compare the handwriting with any of Donnarumma's, since we had none. The Signorina put the letter in the relevant file, a black one.

Friday

While the factory is in a state of ferment, a new wave of examinations and interviews is upon us, and must all be got through if we are to start our holidays before August, as well as a dozen interviews every day with applicants at the porter's lodge. Words, reports, words, reports. Fortunately we are becoming more adept in drawing conclusions from the results of the tests.

The summer, at first fresh with sea breezes and now fiercely hot, is bringing accidents with it. Young Pasquale Giglio, who has an anxious, bird-like face and was brilliant at the psychotechnical tests, but is apt to be *distrait*, has got his foot caught in a crane. I ought to have foreseen something of the sort.

The output of a girl at the machine testing has fallen dramatically, just at the moment when their holiday in mountain air should be approaching. Apart from the greenhouse heat of the assembly-lines she has been got down by a secret love for her brother-in-law, who works behind her, at the benches. Such is the foreman's diagnosis.

There is to be a strike for one hour: Straniero has announced it officially.

One of the drivers has a baby ill with typhoid in a corner of their one-room house, in which eight people are living.

Dattilo spends long hours under the carob-tree in our garden, or lingers in the brief cool of the morning at the viewpoint on the road above, under a pine-tree; he watches me go off in my car, but makes no move to stop me. He is also present when I return at noon, when the sea-breeze rises to meet the quivering mid-summer heat. All the same, he always keeps at a distance; twice only has he spoken again to my wife of the nervous strain of his life at home, the torment of a civil marriage. The girl shuts her eyes as she lies half-naked in her future mother-in-law's bed, and when the old woman is asleep, raps with her knuckles on the wall of his room. If he were allowed to take the examinations he could be at once united with this phantom wife beyond the wall.

Monday

The 15th has gone by without any shots for the Manager. I interviewed a man who after a laconic request for work did not again open his mouth. I explained to him that it was impossible to engage him and he, still silently, stood before me, his eyes full of resentment. He shook his head, and then left without a word.

During these days Donnarumma has not been seen about the entrance.

Following Dattilo's example, a young candidate, a friend of the man at the bathing-huts, and the son of a tailor, trailed my wife on her return from the beach. This morning, at nine o'clock, he was at the threshold of my house, accompanied by his mother; in my office I would have considered him, for he was well spoken, and of a good appearance. But his fat mother was intimating that there would be no further expense for me or my family with regard to clothes; and in an instant threw away twenty years of labour and of good upbringing for her nice-looking boy.

August

A long letter reached me today in the mountains from the Signorina, who will be having her holiday after my return.

"The strike has taken place, on Saturday morning, for an hour, from eleven-thirty onwards; it merely seemed as though work was stopping for the week-end earlier than usual. It was an idea of Straniero's. Thirty-five or forty per cent of the workers supported it. But which department do you think came out almost unanimously? The girls of the machine-testing. Who would have thought that the women would strike? Yet all the girls at the machines calmly left their benches at precisely half-past eleven. Their consciences were clearer than those of the others, on account of their hard labour of the last two years, though it has been of their own choice.

"A strike is a question of conscience. Rather, in the first place, it is a question of interests; but when the time comes, only a clear conscience can enable one to overcome the fear it engenders. I won't bother you with the details: at eleven-thirty the engineers and the industrial experts were looking like thunder, enough to discourage even the works committee. They didn't lift a finger, but went about with stony faces. Two days previously there had been a general meeting in the dining hall. Various reasons for a strike could have been produced, but in my opinion the one they did put up as their main grievance never really gathered support. During the meeting it served as a rallying point, and the majority voted in favour; but when the time came, the majority thought better of it.

"The strikers, having left their work at half-past eleven, went down the drive and scattered under the covered way. I expected them to stay there and wait for their companions, to make a demonstration; but most of them set off home. So it seemed more than ever as though work had simply stopped sooner than usual, by order of the management. I can honestly say that everything went off quietly. As you know, for the present, the real drama here is at the entrance. I am not particularly glad that the strike has partially failed, because any sign of weakness on the part of the workers affects everyone, even the management; but here the pretext that the works committee adopted rested on too uncertain grounds. In my opinion, the works committee declared the strike—not because, in some measure, adequate motives existed—but to demonstrate its own importance, rather than to bring grievances to light. Our workers cannot forget the advantages they enjoy here; they are intelligent, and only have to look around them.

"And yet, men in the mass become enigmatic; who can know what they are thinking, each one of them? They often become dominated by some fixed idea, and in a meeting find themselves all of one mind; but the moment that fear begins to force them to choose between the management and the works committee, the needle of the balance begins to oscillate. The slightest thing is enough to make it go one way or the other. The whole of Festa's department came out on strike, because Festa himself, the head of it, was a striker: which goes to prove the importance of the heads. What is the management going to do about Festa?

"It is my belief that up to the last moment most of the workers were undecided; they looked doubtfully at one another, and it would have taken very little to make them either stay or go. It was a dramatic moment. Perhaps the test of a strike is always educative, even for those who stay at work.

"There is something justifiable about every strike, even if only as an affirmation of the right to strike. Do you think me a revolutionary? A strike makes one face one's own problems and makes one think, during the long hours between the decision and the carrying out of it. When, the previous day, I read the management's notices on the boards by the dining-room, explaining why the award of a bonus on profits would not be justified, and the resolution of the works committee declaring the opposite, I had a strange feeling . . . I suffered from the clash between the two points of view.

"You will ask me, what did I do? I stayed at work. In this firm, we of the personnel office feel close to the workers; perhaps they put us in the personnel office just because our sympathies are with them. Otherwise, instead of you, they might call in a policeman. But that I, of the personnel office, should go on strike seemed to me absurd. It would be illogical. Before striking I would have to get transferred elsewhere.

Remaining in the personnel office, since it is the work for which we are cut out, and accepting this human responsibility because it is what we best like, implies a sacrifice. I abstained from striking not out of political or trades union motives, but out of loyalty to the management. When I want to strike, I shall ask to be put where I dislike the work. But if I enjoy the privilege of finding satisfaction in my work, I must pay morally for it. Though there certainly is an inner sense of contradiction . . ."

Up here, among the green fir trees, Santa Maria seems very far away. Santa Maria must be burning and stagnating in the August heat. In my imagination I can see the steep rocky coast on either hand, with its picturesque villages, the islands with their famous outlines, the classical ruins and the striking natural phenomena of a land long known to history: with the most original people in the world. An ideal place for long, indolent summer holidays, or for rapid sightseeing by train or boat.

But Torre has sixty thousand inhabitants, and the little town of Santa Maria forty thousand; in this strip of coast the population is as dense as in the most thickly populated provinces of China.

Such a district should be an entirely industrial one if it is to live, even if it enjoys the least industrial reputation in the world.

The sea does not help; it has been despoiled, this noble, magnificent and ancient sea. When, among our applicants, a fisherman turns up, he seems a survivor from former times. Nor are there many seamen; very few of the ancient near-by towns still draw mercantile wealth from the sea. Yet in barbarous, Saracen Santa Maria, are there no sea-farers left? I do not remember any candidate who boasted his adventures on the ocean, who brought a whiff of briny air with him: the fishermen's sons have no wish to be fishermen, and the few boats one sees belong to owners who use the old mariners as paid workers.

As far as Naples, until the fields of ancient lava begin, the coastal strip is too narrow for satisfactory agricultural development; the sub-terranean fires reach nearly to the earth's surface, and one almost finds them if one digs a hole, as one does water in a valley. There is also a redundance of ruins, lakes, spent volcanic craters, caves of the Sibyl and baths of Agrippina. The increasing population fills more and more space for living, not cultivation, as on the outskirts of a city. It ought to move beyond the line of volcanic peaks behind the coast and spread into the fertile plain inland. But even this plain is becoming over-crowded, so that the people emigrate towards the factories on the coast, which are themselves undergoing an economic crisis. We have far more interviews with peasants from the villages of the interior than with fishermen.

Today Santa Maria, without the markets open to it in classical times, without support from the sea, has no reason for being where it is: but it now has too intense a life of its own for one even to imagine the population emigrating or being transported elsewhere.

Thus, on the one hand we think them dazed, suffocated, by their natural surroundings, yet satisfied with a happiness of their own that it would be a pity to destroy; and on the other we know that their needs, more than those of any other southern Italian population, are clearly urban. It is precisely this people, so free and undisciplined, so instinctive in their reactions, who require an industrial social order, and potentially they have already created one. Unintentionally, they have created it by their high birth-rate, as though full industrialization by the State were already here, as though private capital from the north were on the spot, boldly seeking out new reservoirs of human labour; as though the continents were wide open to immigration.

Here a labour force is being wasted for lack of work, an industrial population is idle, without industry. This is the dramatic situation in the vicinity and in Naples, with its splendid palaces and dreadful slums; an ancient capital that has gone down with the general deterioration of the south.

As to the high birth-rate, this is not the cause but the consequence of poverty. No one has ever said to one of our workers: "Don't have so many children. Be careful." Or: "You are twenty-five years old and the other day your mother had another baby. What on earth can your father be thinking of?" Or: "Very well, you are unemployed; you have three unemployed brothers, and you have been married for three years. Then why, why, have you three children already? Is it our fault? Are you blaming the factory for your desperate case, are you blaming the management?"

CHAPTER XIII

First Monday in September

ON THE FIRST morning after my holiday, the sea, no longer flat as a board beneath the summer sun, was ruffled by a fresh breeze. Dattilo was on guard under the pines on the hillside. My car slowed down near the turning on to the high-road, and he came forward, raised his hand, then took another step towards me. For the last week or so he has left his house early every morning, to spend his days up there. The slowing-down of my car at the corner made him think I was about to stop, and he came forward again; I saw his small round head near me at the window, with his little eyes and sunken cheeks; he gave me a smile that was more of a grimace. I passed him and he remained standing in the middle of the road.

At the crossroads to Santa Maria, Accettura appeared on the footpath, as dark and wizened as ever. He was walking towards the porters' lodge, and tried to stop me. I accelerated past his tattered figure and raised hand. Still further on, on the opposite pavement, Chiodo and his son were walking with bent heads, and so hurriedly that they saw nothing around them, not even me.

On the low wall at the roadside, with a small crowd of newcomers, Donnarumma was sitting, with a preoccupied air. I caught sight of him as I entered the gates to receive Bellomo's ample salute as I passed; a cheerful but sympathetic greeting for one's return from a holiday.

In celebration of my reappearance, Bellomo had cleared the entrance of applicants: they were all outside, leaning against the wall and waiting for orders.

Suddenly a tall man dressed in greenish brown, with a large, wrinkled face, darted out from behind a column of the covered way. He raised his hands in front of my car, as Bellomo sprang from his cabin. This time I had to stop.

The man, leaning towards my window, struck himself on the chest. "What's the matter with my face, what's the matter with it?" he asked, as I opened the window to look at him. I saw nothing odd about his face.

"What is wrong with my face, what makes it so distasteful to your illustrious lordship, that I have never had the honour of being received?"

So now we were face to face. This was the man they call Papa.

Tuesday

For months, Luigi Papaleo, known as Papa, has been told he cannot be given work here. He was a labourer employed by the building firm that put up the factory, during which work he unfortunately suffered a blow on the head from a falling beam. I only knew him by repute, because the porters were careful to send him away without always informing the personnel office.

I was trapped yesterday, with the scene about his face.

"I'll look at your application again . . ." I said to him.

"Have a look at it, Doctor," he replied gravely, his voice loud and hoarse. "Have a look at it, because a serious injustice has been committed, not against me, but against justice itself. You see this factory?" My window was open, and Bellomo, intimidated by Papa's success in getting into conversation with me, did not interrupt. "You see this factory? It was not made with water." Pause. "It was not made with cement and water," he went on. I was conscious that behind my back Donnarumma and the others were approaching from the wall, taking advantage of my having stopped; and that from the pavement Chiodo and his son were following them. "It was made with cement and sweat, the sweat of all of us labourers. Sweat lasts better than water. In fact, you can see what a fine factory it is."

"It is true that . . ."

"There, even you know this is true. However, you are quite right, you are quite right," he declaimed, waving his arm, and taking charge of the argument, as he stared at me. "They sweated, but then they were only ignorant workmen, they knew nothing about psychotechnology, they're no use as mechanics."

"Then you understand that too."

In his excitement he struck a column of the covered way with his fist. "But this factory, this wall, is not made with my sweat."

"Papaleo . . ."

"You may not know it, Doctor," he declared, backing away with a dramatic air. "It was made with my blood." He leant forward with bent head, his hand on his hair. "Blood from here, blood from here. Blood from my head."

With both hands he parted his hair to show the upper part of the cranium. "The wound is as big as a hand. Feel it. The beam fell from a height of ten metres. Feel it." I couldn't really bring myself to touch it.

"Luckily you are cured now . . ."

"Perfectly cured . . ." He raised his head. "All the same, I left something behind me." He smiled again. "A piece of my brain has remained in the wall of this factory. Some people try to make out that the brain I still have is no good . . . Doctor, they tell you I'm mad."

"That's not true."

"All the same, only a man not right in the head would be refused even one interview by your lordship. You've received them all, men, women, children, but only Papa has never had an interview. What is wrong with my face?" He struck himself again on the breast, while his eyes remained clouded, afflicted.

"I myself will look up your application."

"You are the only one," he proclaimed, "the only one who does not wade in my blood. I await justice from you."

I was finally able to continue up the drive.

"Crazy?" exploded the Signorina, standing in my office and staring at the sea in her anger. "He was more crazy before he had the accident. Oh, you don't know Papa! He flares up like a match. If anything, he's better now, since the beam fell on his head."

Among other innovations in the factory since the holidays, I found Ugo at the assembly-lines. He was at the end of the room, at one of the benches where they insert the springs into the little containers . . . My work. He was actually sitting between the young man from Liguria—who has not been replaced by any woman and who still carries on at the same rapid rate—and the secondary schoolboy from Santa Maria, who now works with speed and concentrated attention. He has gained confidence at the benches, but he remains solitary in his new status as a worker, which he accepts unquestioningly.

I did not at first recognize Ugo, wrapped up in an overall that, still stiff with starch, was too big for him, but his long face and red, dry skin betrayed him. I drew near: his thin fingers were shaking, and his hands felt for the springs like those of a blind man. He tried to put on speed and struck the mechanism awkwardly; I smiled at him and he did not respond. He is still afraid. But he is now decent, clean, his dissolution averted. The factory is bringing him out, and will be the salvation of this well-behaved young man.

Perhaps it is useless to ask oneself whether the workers taken into this factory, those who have won their way through the intelligence tests, are now happy, or whether they are destined to become unhappy and disappointed. All the same, one wonders.

The factory doctor, who knows their secrets better than anyone else, gives this preliminary reply. It depends on whether they have experience of other factories, whether they have worked elsewhere; or whether it is here that they are for the first time faced with eight full hours of mass-production work and scientific organization. A manual labourer who had been in the iron works, rather elderly and not very fit, had replied to the doctor, who asked him if he suffered from the heat processes: "Doctor, compared with what I did before, this cellulosing work is like being in a ladies' sitting-room." But the young men, who had been unemployed for years but free to walk about Santa Maria, among their friends, their families, or beside the sea, may perhaps—once the thrill of being engaged here has worn off—fail to develop, in the course of years, that sense of a closed, collective factory life that is second nature to a working community. Workers have their traditions no less than the nobles.

We are providing the sociologists with a flourishing virgin field for study. They can examine here not only the relations between modern industry and the south, but also internal industrial problems, of historical interest. In our factory, automation can already be glimpsed; but in the meantime it is automatism that rules the day, the phase that does not as yet reintegrate the fragmentation of the work (with each man doing a small fraction of the productive process, and always the same one) and which, in fact, having done away with the old technique, is now breaking the process up more and more.

How far will it continue to do so? As far as the optimum of output. When—and it is already to be seen—the worker becomes tired and weakened by the excessive simplicity and monotony of his allotted task, then ways of joining up the work again will be thought out, to make it less automatic and more varied.

In the meantime, various views are held about this intensity of automatism, for many modern psychologists take a passionate interest in it; less so the workers at the benches and the machines.

Here, beside me, the southerner who has come back from Liguria in the north is certainly putting up with a monotonous job: precisely the type of work that has been so much studied and which, according to some writers, leads to the annihilation of all thought and an unhealthy play of phantasy. It should not be forgotten, however, that other experts consider this very monotony beneficial; because it liberates the imagination and therefore makes man's spirit free. At this point the theories again diverge: one is that this liberty of the mind gives the worker an opportunity to dedicate his time to reflection, especially to thinking about politics, and therefore helps to mature him; the other that freedom to use his mind is dangerous, because the labour force may use it to think ill of the employers and to brood on reasons for revolt. While it is easy to imagine to which vision of the world the two schools of thought belong, I myself cannot tell, for instance, whether either applies to the young Ligurian. Even if I watch him, as now, from two paces away.

Another school has come to a sort of judgment of Solomon: it holds that certain individuals take easily to automatic monotony and prefer it, while others do not; and that this is a question of temperament. The task of the psycho-technical expert is to pick out the former for mass-production work, and to keep the latter away from it. If this psychological diagnosis is valid, it makes the choice an inexorable, diabolic one; because those who are thought to be suited to monotonous work would have no hope of ever escaping from it.

And then, there is technical progress. According to the most advanced of these thinkers, technical progress will reach incredible reductions in working hours; to 36, 30, 20 hours a week, one single day in the week: for a task so light and automatic that one will hardly be aware of doing it; or with workers so intelligent that they will all be sitting in their white overalls, book in hand, at the controls. To those of us who are continually involved in the question of overtime in the factory, these days seem far away. But sociologists are already concerned with the question of free time, and are thinking out how to "plan" it: in other words, how not to make it more free.

A woman working-class writer has said some very hard things about free time; but has she told us the whole truth about factories? Here, in the heart of a factory, we often consider this problem of free time, but we do not succeed in solving it; because of changing conditions, and because, although I often pass behind our workers at the machines, their real thoughts still elude me. Sociology is always trying to find a method for seeking them out, and then pursues it. But if I try to work at the presses, I am not one of the workers. If I question them, they may perhaps lie to me. If I observe them, I can describe them, but not understand them. If I try to imagine what goes on in their heads, I may invent a stream of thought that is not theirs. They ought to be able to express themselves; and yet, the moment they do so, they break away from that silence which is characteristic of the workers' condition, a condition to be deduced only by certain indirect signs in their life outside the factory. The famous woman worker mentioned above is of the opinion that in automatism a part of the human attention must always be used: the man's suffering is due to the fact that his thoughts could, might be able, to free themselves, but are always pulled back by the cord that holds them to the machine. The worst, the most de-grading kind of freedom is this sham, divided freedom, to which free time is useless. She believes that a reduction in working-hours is morally wrong. Since the life of workers, physically and mentally, is in their work, what can they find to feed their minds on, outside the factory? They must be free in their work, that is, in the moment in which they truly live; and free time does not make sense if it is not cut from their work.

The sombre Marxist theme of the alienation of the workers from society is to be discerned at the root of all these interpretations. Owing to the fact that they do not own the means of production, or because of scientific organization and the sub-division of labour—in other words, owing to the capitalist system (and a problem also in a Socialist society) —the worker is kept apart and isolated in a responsibility so fragmented and remote from any ultimate aims as to violate his instincts, his will and his intelligence. According to Marxist theory, all the human relations in the world cannot break down this barrier.

Chronic unemployment, instead, really does produce this division in the community: it is unemployment here, at Santa Maria, that is the true, historic cause of the cutting-off of the worker from society, and it is unemployment that underlies every industrial problem, co-existent, though it may be, with an industrial social order.

Ugo is not cut off from life by this bench: it is with it that he enters into life. He might have chanced upon a job that was less monotonous and more human. But what other jobs could he find in his home town? Industrial conditions are usually compared with those of the artisan class, and the idea of the industrial workers' segregation from life has arisen in the wake of the decline of an artisan economy. But if you look around you here, you will see very little sign of an artisan class.

To become, suddenly, a mechanical worker after having been un-employed seems a veritable miracle here, whereas elsewhere it is a natural fate for an individual belonging to a particular class. And here, much more than elsewhere, the workers feel a pride in their factory and in their own status as part of a great firm; every form, in fact, of working-class snobbery develops, alongside the discipline and bore-dom of their work, and their segregation from their fellows. Through this factory one sees "the working-class social inferiority complex"— to quote a well-known writer on this subject—"giving rise to a legal organization which produces new customs, and becomes a factor of enthusiasm instead of depression". One can see it all the time: more-over, one can see it being transformed into a sense of innate merit, a kind of aristocracy, from which those who have been excluded suffer because they remain plebeians, and of which the chosen few boast with an egoistic and bourgeois pride in their status.

On the other hand, the young men here have a dread of becoming peasants, and the country people a contempt for trade and shopkeeping. No other respect-worthy occupation exists save this, of being a mechanical worker. The peasants who break their backs in the intensive culture of tomatoes along the coast ought to feel far less cut off from the life around them, although they, like the factory workers, do not own the means of production: but at least they care for their products from beginning to end, sowing them, watching them grow and gathering the fruit (which, in the end, the middle-men buy at their own price). Yet a tomato-grower would jump at the chance to enter our factory.

They all feel that the factory offers them security, and that it is the key to proletarian progress, as a career is to the bourgeois; it ties them to the machine, but it brings them liberation in other ways, even if only in restoring to them the right as men to make complaints. Many, soon, will be making use of this right: the breath of revolt is already to be felt in our factory, as it was in July, even though on mistaken grounds. They will not be happy. But when I pass through the factory I do not feel that I am going through ranks of men cut off from the world.

It is also because the majority of them are young, like the factory itself; they are a body of workers not stratified, and not as yet resigned; one does not see the deterioration, the stubborn rebelliousness of the older workers in the north, nor the distressing discord between young and old. Here there are always young faces bowed over their work, but not consumed by it.

Everyone now wants to know how this body of predominantly untrained workers is managing to adapt itself to the standards of a northern industry so highly specialized as ours. That the men of Santa Maria should, in fact, be producing these fine, delicate machines has fired the imagination of employers, journalists and intellectuals. The questions are never-ending: do these southerners really know how to work? What is their output? Is it greater or less than that of the workers in northern Italy?

I always try to give a fair answer, but one does not exist. We have such a wide choice. We can select the very best and discard such an infinite number that it is difficult to make comparisons between this body of young, picked workers of the south and an average, mixed labour force in the north, or elsewhere. This is the first difficulty.

The second is that where there is a tendency towards scientific organization, very little room is left for nature, for temperamental diversity. The worker at the machines or the benches, even at Santa Maria, is held in the same grip that would hold him at Turin or anywhere else. Outside, they are what centuries of history and primitive beliefs have made them, intelligent but capricious, dignified but disorderly: all the usual commonplaces about the south return to my mind as true. A people that loves song, a people moved more by prejudice than by reality, who prefer the luxuries to the necessities of life; a people who have no money but would not know how to spend it if they had, and who delight in flights of fancy rather than in plain facts. History, having deformed them, fully justifies them, but historical justification cannot redeem them either today or tomorrow, because an evil is an evil, whether there is a reason for it or not; and one cannot always be thinking of the reason. The evil becomes an injury, and festers.

Instead, in the factory, they improve, and we with them. We get to understand one another and to grow more alike, united as we are by the same aim to produce; in other words, by the same fate. When we are all at our posts, their pyrotechnical displays of temper die down, and our cold, foolish prejudices are warmed into humanity. The factory makes men equal, smoothes out ill-temper and reduces faults of character. The organizers from the north who, when they first arrived, wore the air of colonial administrators have given it up, and have begun to understand.

There is always, throughout the factory, the same silence of people who are working against time, a compulsion that, in itself, is a kind of enslavement; but, nowhere else, as here, does the reverse side of this necessary slavery appear so clearly: the grim dignity of these workers as, day by day, they forge their way to freedom.

CHAPTER XIV

Wednesday

WHAT HAD PAPALEO been like, before the beam fell on him? Was he already queer in the head, or was it the accident? The engineer who had watched the construction of the building and who now sees to its upkeep remembers Papaleo well, as a labourer who would suddenly turn on a companion and threaten him with a pick; but he was strong, and able to take on very heavy work. And now? He had been passed as sixty per cent unfit, so it must be true that the beam had more than halved his abilities.

The engineer's assistant did not agree: "Papa exploits his injury. He had the eyes of a madman before the accident. He often used to have brainstorms."

"But he was capable of working?"

"Yes, he could work."

"Would you take him back?"

"I'd keep him away, as far as possible. He drinks."

"Did he drink before?"

"I don't know. I've never seen him drinking, myself."

Perhaps, before, he was only neurasthenic. Perhaps Signorina S. would be able to explain things; so I waited for her return from the employment bureau in the town.

Three thousand official unemployed are beating on that door. Their names are registered, but many of them are always hanging about there. One of these days, when the Signorina arrives, there will be an outbreak of violence; for this reason she is always taken there by Santoro, the strongest driver we have.

Signorina S. is a highly strung woman, but full of courage; her own zeal for work often leaves her very tired, and the more tired she is the more zealous she becomes: but in the midst of our adventures here she has never shown fear. For a long time she has borne the brunt of our difficulties and has surmounted them, but in so doing, she has won a reputation for strictness (though this would be easy to disprove) and has been held responsible for certain unexpected decisions in matters where many of us, too, would have lost our way.

It is essential to have her opinion of Papa, because she tells the truth without too many doubts and subtleties. She always knows the pros and cons of every problem, and never loses her head, as she runs from one office to another. We all lean on her.

This time she returned from the employment bureau like a whirlwind, quite beside herself. For once she seemed really shaken. Striding into my room, with a pale face, she insisted on something being done at once. The fear underlying her anger made her pitiable.

"Donnarumma," she said. "It's Donnarumma again." She would not even sit down.

"I was coming from the employment bureau in the car, with Santoro." The employment bureau is a tragedy; it is the fourth, fifth, sixth power in a poor town. "At the entrance here—just at the gates— Donnarumma came up when Santoro had to slow down to turn. He made for my side of the car."

"Wasn't Bellomo there?"

"He was sleeping, wasn't he? He's been doing night-duty. There was another . . . that other . . . that nit-wit." For a moment she paused to recall the guard's name. Then her eyes clouded once more, and she trembled imperceptibly.

"Donnarumma," she went on in a strangled voice, "Donnarumma made a leap at the car and reached at my throat, through the window. He tried to throttle me."

"But what was Santoro doing?"

"He accelerated, Donnarumma had to pull his arm away, otherwise it would have been broken." She was still suffering from shock, but she was not the sort to faint. Already the assault began to appear to her as just an episode in her work, an incident to be liquidated in due course. But it was one thing to be threatened by Donnarumma, and another actually to feel his hand on her throat. She returned to her room, though she could not settle to her work. I pressed her to sit down and rest, and said: "We'll get the police, at once. This time we'll lodge a complaint. Sit down, Signorina, and calm yourself."

Seated, she nodded in agreement. Papa's fate, too, was sealed.

Saturday

Several days of quiet have followed the crisis; a crisis that seemed to open a void around us. Once the Manager had heard the Signorina's story and had telephoned to the police, the business of a "denunciation" was started, and now keeps the porters' lodge clear of its familiar figures. Only Dattilo's small afflicted head peers out from behind a pine-tree on my hillside, to give me a disappointed smile. It was raining today. September is cooling off. Along the main road, but nearer

the crossroads to Santa Maria than the factory and not coming in our
direction, I passed Donnarumma. He was wearing a black jacket over
his jersey, with the collar up, and was walking slowly, intent on his
own affairs, like any other hapless unemployed worker.

Monday

Although a "denunciation" is likely to rouse animosity against us
rather than to afford us protection, the Signorina has recovered her
good spirits, and after a Sunday's repose has almost forgotten the
incident.

Donnarumma, on the other hand, as he sees the distance between
himself and us becoming always greater, must be consumed with grim
paranoiac exasperation: it is alarming to think of him alone in his
blind wrath, denounced to the police, his thoughts simmering in his
thick head. But the Signorina, almost as though to prove that she fears
nothing, wants Gallina interviewed.

For some months letters have been arriving from this Gallina. "You
are just a lot of morons. My girl has left me, and it's all your fault.
You are morons not to engage me." Having received a negative
reply to his application he was venting his rage on the personnel
office and the factory.

He presented himself unexpectedly this afternoon to Bellomo, who
telephoned through to us. The Signorina laughed at once: "It's the
man who calls us morons. I'd like to see his face."

Tall and strong, young Gallina came into my room, while the
Signorina sat with me behind my desk. "So here you are," she said to
him. "Now you find yourself in the presence of at least two morons."
Gallina did not react, but looked sullenly at her as she went on: "Why
do you want to work in a factory run by morons?"

Dressed in a light-coloured suit with wide shoulders, shabby but
smartened up by a white tie on his blue shirt, he was a bit of a dandy.
He screwed up his eyes and said: "I gave my reasons in my letter . . .
private . . . intimate reasons."

"You are alluding," asked the Signorina, "to the person who has
betrayed you?"

"Signorina . . . She hasn't exactly betrayed . . ."

"The doctor, here, thinks as I do that a woman should stand by you
in misfortune. If you deserve it."

"Certainly, if you deserve it."

Balancing the weight of his body on one foot, Gallina the seducer
turned his eyes quickly towards me as I spoke, then looked again at

the Signorina. "Perhaps, Doctor, she wasn't . . . she isn't . . . a woman of feeling, I mean a woman . . ."

"And what do you mean?"

"I mean a woman not materially minded. Spiritual." The thought crossed my mind that perhaps he would make something of the examinations.

"Ah, you like them to be spiritual?" The Signorina, surprised, pressed home the advantage. "And you, do you think yourself spiritual in writing these letters? Or spirited?" The young dandy understood; he gave a half-laugh, and made a gesture with his hands as though asking for forgiveness.

Then he said bitterly: "You speak like that because I have no recommendation."

At once the Signorina hardened.

"Enough of these recommendations!"

"I've no recommendation, either from senators or bishops," he retorted arrogantly.

"Certainly, a bishop would be unlikely to recommend you."

"Not me. The others. You only accept the ones that have the bishop's cross on their applications."

"What crosses, what crosses and what bishops?" I demanded.

"Yes, Doctor. They take their applications to a bishop, he puts his cross on it and you engage them."

"Do you mean the cross that a bishop puts beside his signature?"

"Not beside the signature. Above the application."

"That's enough," said the Signorina. "That's enough!"

But he stayed and was not sent away. The ingenuous, insidious myth of the crosses, the myth of the recommendations, had found its way into Gallina's sceptical mind; but why should one think that he might not be a good worker, strong and receptive, better than his letters? Ought we to lose him? The Signorina, having trapped him with his own words, now fell silent.

Naturally he feared our silence, our most dangerous weapon. Then opening wide his arms he made a resolute gesture of renunciation: "I want to forget it all . . ." The Signorina's face lit up, since he was apparently aknowledging defeat. "I want to forget everything I wrote in my letters."

"Ah, then we can forget it too."

"I have forgotten it all, all," he decided, convinced that from this humiliation would come his immediate engagement, with special understanding for him, since we would not be cruel and he was obviously a superior type of applicant.

"We will see."

But the Signorina herself has written *No* on his papers. He had gone out, with a valiant swing of his shoulders, in the smart suit that concealed the usual signs of poverty; a big, slippery fish, come like all the rest to be caught in the usual net.

Tuesday

On my way to the laboratory I saw Donnarumma again. He was walking on the other side of the road and might have been about to cross it in order to spy on us through the windows.

I called to him from the gateway. He approached with his usual stony expression. Bellomo was present at our meeting, watching us, amazed, from his cabin; and another guard emerged from a room on the corridor and from his torpor. Standing at the opening into the corridor and with these two witnesses at a distance, I endeavoured to present a bold front to Donnarumma.

Without any show of emotion he began at once: "I have sent in my application. By registered post."

"We haven't received it."

"I took it to the post office the day before yesterday."

"Why haven't we had it?"

"Because you want to do for me. You've set the police on to me."

"We have not had the application. Someone is lying."

Beneath his low forehead, Donnarumma's expressionless eyes clouded.

"You say I'm lying?" he muttered. His voice was hoarse, and his chest swelled as he clenched his fists.

"Everyone sends in an application except you. Why? Why must you be different from the rest?"

"I went to the post office. I went. I've got the receipt at home."

"We have received nothing."

"When you get it, will I be given the tests?" he asked with a natural air, as though we were meeting for the first time.

"First we consider your application. Then we send you a written reply."

"You send a reply to the police."

"You laid hands on the Signorina."

"It's she who has burnt my application."

"We will wait for the application to arrive." I left him standing there, and went on to the laboratory, but with no hope of a solution. Donnarumma still waited; he defied us with such stubborn obstinacy that he seemed untouched by his own wrath. Santoro, coming out of the laboratory went towards him, and slowly drove him away, as though clearing the air of the corridor.

Thursday

Another anonymous letter in the post, but nothing from Donnarumma. "If you engage Antonio Del Carmine before the 1st October we will set fire to the factory." The handwriting of every letter in the black file resembles the rest, but it is merely that of all the semi-illiterates in the country.

Why this incendiarism on account of Del Carmine?

"How do they know that we have promised to take him on?" the Manager asked me.

"I don't know anything about this Del Carmine."

"But yes . . . I meant to speak to you about him. He is the brother of the girl who works here, Anna Del Carmine. He is a carabineer who wants to leave the force. Bellomo is always complaining that he hasn't enough guards. The girl came to me in tears about her brother and I told her to send him here. We could do with an ex-carabineer."

"Yes . . ."

"The girl swore that she wouldn't breathe a word of it to anyone, either here or in the town." The Manager was stubbing the ends of his cigarettes with a worried look on his face. "She told me her brother's story. It's a particularly unfortunate family . . ." He gave a deprecatory smile, as though to excuse himself. "Even though you have come across so many families who are particularly unfortunate . . ."

"Yes, indeed . . ."

"But Anna Del Carmine deserves some recompense. She is an extremely good worker."

"I know."

"She promised me to say nothing of it. A young woman like her ought to be able to hold her tongue." He went on, gloomily: "A quiet, shy girl. I made it a condition, if she wanted to help her brother . . . I don't understand how a girl like her . . . Now it would serve her right . . ."

"She wasn't able to resist the temptation. At Santa Maria it would not be humanly possible to keep such a promise secret."

"Yes, you know them well, now," he said, as though he himself were isolated in his position.

"We know one another. I don't know whether it helps."

"It helps."

"The girl couldn't hold out. A promise from the Manager is worth all the gold in the world. You can't imagine how the Del Carmine family is now increasing in prestige, in pride, in hope for the future . . ." The Manager was lighting and extinguishing his cigarettes one after the other, deep in thought.

"Should we do anything about the anonymous letter?" I asked.

"I don't think we shall go up in flames. The Del Carmine woman is more important." He drily indicated the essential point, and I rose and went towards the door. Taking another cigarette from the packet, he gave me a friendly or perhaps remorseful look, slightly shaking his head: "Ah, I wanted to tell you a funny story. The day before yesterday I was questioning one of your candidates. Severely. I was looking closely at him, and instead of my cigarette I put my pen in my mouth. He was convulsed with laughter. After that, the interview with the Manager was rather a waste of time, don't you think?"

CHAPTER XV

Examinations and interviews for the whole week. We are trying out a new "battery" of tests, or rather, of material, sent us by our headquarters. They are changed and improved continually, according to the most modern methods. Behind every test—which may seem little more than a game—lie years of scientific work. We are improving the apparatus. Much work is being planned regarding the comparison between examination results and subsequent, periodic evaluation of the worker in the factory. To the lay mind this might seem quite a simple matter: but, in fact, it is a most arduous operation, because we run the risk of comparing what is incommensurable; the diverse aspects of a man, let us say, with geometrical forms, figures with words. And the appraisement of factory workers, too, requires a special technique; who is to do it, who is to check it? Are we to rely on statistics or on opinions? We cannot organize it here until the pressure on our gates, which uses up our energies, is relaxed.

The Manager and I often talk of this evaluation and our sociological education suffers from the necessity of postponing it continually because of our undertaking to interview the men at the entrance. I sometimes ask myself whether I am wasting my time.

But yesterday the cashier, a man whose probity and loyalty to the firm are unquestionable—who lives in the very heart of Santa Maria and who likes to feel that he is a link between us and the little town —said that the people there were grateful to us for receiving the applicants one by one.

It means that the people understand, without realizing it, the connection between the special quality of our factory and the value of the *No* given with so many empty words of explanation: the refusal which everyone received in the dark days, and which it seemed mad and pointless to go on repeating.

"What about Donnarumma?" I asked him.

"Oh, Donnarumma is crazy, Doctor."

Every morning a little flock of men, shifty and dejected, muddle-minded or intelligent—among them perhaps a long-haired girl, a boy with the face of a child, a grey-haired man or an illiterate fisherman as usual called in by mistake, or else a city man come down in the world, dressed in a town suit—ends up in the laboratory, which is often half dark owing to the blinds being drawn on account of Donnarumma's attempts at ambushing us.

With the passing of time, and the tough skin that one has to grow, we have become industrial psychologists, school-teachers, disciplinarians, sadists, the Signorina and I. We now have a young girl as an assistant, who sees to the alarm-clock and deals out clean sheets of paper. She wears a provocative skirt that swings above her knees, but they never look at her legs: the alarm-clock keeps their heads bent over their tests. There is nothing like these examinations for turning their thoughts away from sex, a subject that psychotechnology does not investigate.

Some confusion is caused by a new test consisting of coloured cubes in small cellophane bags, which are distributed, desk by desk. They resemble the cubes that are given to children to play with. The candidates open the bags and spread them out on the desks. In a given time these have to be composed into certain figures, reproduced from printed diagrams. There is a tendency to laugh, but fear overcomes it. Since it is a new test, we have to compare its results with those of former experiments, now given up. But we are again aware of the difficulty of applying this test to a mixed group of middle-aged men, girls and youths. In the north they only use it for the boy trainees.

I have naturally resumed my interviews after the tests, to carry further the interpretation of the marks. These are registered on an apparatus with a pen-point which draws a line between them on squared paper. It goes zigzag, with bulges to the right in the case of positive results, to the left in negative, and straight where the balance is good. The lines gives the mathematical profile of the man and of his aptitudes, which can in this way be seen in a flash, as one sees a face.

One looks in it for what is unchanging and for similarity of abilities: success in the "Spatial" test for mechanical aptitude is often accompanied by victory in the tests of manual ability. This relationship between abstract, mechanical aptitudes and manual dexterity ought to provide a favourable forecast for a mechanical worker. But verbal and non-verbal intellectual ability must not be passed over; for this is an indication of general intelligence, the "G" factor, which over-rides all else.

In analysing the tests, it can be seen that they all tend to show one factor more than others—the Numerical, the Spatial, etc.; but the "G" factor, the mysterious general intelligence is found mixed with others in every test, as well as in its pure state in some of them. It is the ubiquity of intelligence that we respect and recognize as our guide in all selecting.

Even the engineers never tire nowadays of demanding intelligence. They would rather have intelligence than qualifications, experience, the backbone of factory life. They say: Who gave him his diploma? What is it to me? Or, Where would you yourself put a stupid manual worker? The engineers are no longer satisfied with primary schooling in a young applicant; they want at least three years of lower secondary schooling; they do not, however, want failed clerical workers, who, at the benches or the machines, are still apt to dream of the paradise of office work.

In seeking the fundamental factors of men's abilities, in trying to define them—and in constructing tests to discover these factors—one attempts to distinguish, in the elusive material of a man and an inhabitant of Santa Maria, the perfect worker. For his sake one scans the horizon to find a technique of the spirit; in forecasting a man's future one is forced to raise some kind of barrier against the mysterious feelings with which men affect one another, letting themselves be carried away by a momentary emotion. Man is not an object, a tree, a planet . . . But we can, at least, believe that psychotechnology helps us not to lose our way.

I keep the blue chart with the candidate's profile of aptitudes half hidden in his file as I glance at him and start a conversation. The same, stale words come and go, yet with each new applicant they take on new life and have a different sound. Each man gives his own colouring to them; the encounter may seem just like the previous one until by a gesture, a phrase, a silence—or more rarely by the telling of a whole story—the man himself is revealed and unconsciously a verdict is formed.

The conversation is vague; anyone present might think it banal. Questions with a thrust to them, or a psychological basis (such as, "You don't love your father?") are rare. They describe the natural surroundings of their homes or the near-by streets. I am careful about important points, such as distances and directions. We speak of the films they like: thrillers, historical films, Westerns, romantic costume plays, and American adventures. No neo-realism for them. If a novel-reader turns up, his preferences are much the same as those in Rome or Milan. They do not read the daily papers, but the illustrated weeklies are passed from hand to hand. Anything serves for our talk. And, it may be from habit, experience or intuition, by the time a quarter of an hour has passed some positive conclusion has been come to in my mind, like a face that appears through the mist. Which is most valuable, this intuition or the psycho-technical methods of estimating? We rely now on one, now on the other: but perhaps if the day were to come when there was not time for both, one would choose the human, empirical judgment. On the one hand I have the marks for Reasoning, Memory, Concentrated Attention, Spatial Visualization, Digital Skill, etc.; and on the other, an impression that takes these marks into account but that merges into a general feeling about the man, guided perhaps by certain indications of his mental level, know-ledge of school subjects, capacity for observation and attention, mechanical understanding, or manual ability. From these I may be able to forecast his capacity for learning, the possible development of his character, and his suitability for the assembly-lines or the work-shop or for care of the machines.

The prognosis is the most difficult, for in it lies all the doubt and all the risk. At times it seems that the great category of average men com-prises all the candidates. It is then that the ability of the interviewer to be "impressed" becomes blunted. There seems nothing to choose between them.

But after all, perhaps this particular rogue might become an honest man in the factory . . . Why won't this other, who has considerable mechanical aptitude, speak a word—what is he afraid of? Would this intelligent boy stick factory work for more than three months? The man who stands sweating before my table and has a nervous twitch may be able to transform himself into something different, might turn out to be as strong as anyone else . . .

But, in the end, so long a line of men eliminates the marginal, uncertain cases, those with whom one feels an indefinable sympathy. During the afternoon, ten interviews become merged into one single piece of work, technical like any other, to be executed as well as possible, all scruples eliminated. Until at last the interviewer, feeling a little drunk, rises and stretches himself. It is only human not to remember.

Except that one will never be able to forget the unending procession of eyes.

Later, driving along the high-road to the city or to Castello—Santa Maria is better avoided for the moment—among similar men who might have come today or may come tomorrow—the stories told me come thronging back to my mind. Please remember me, Doctor, I'd manage. I'll do any sort of work, Doctor. I only have a job twice a week, driving a car. I work in a private factory: there's only work for three months in the year. In the summer I act as attendant at the baths. Two thousand five hundred, four thousand *lire* a week. I'd do any kind of work. Even cleaning . . . Put me to clean out the lavatories, Doctor.

Monday

The life-histories weigh more with one than good judgment.

Father, disabled. Mother, housewife. Three brothers: one insane, another a student, another unemployed. A sister at home. The fourth brother stands before me.

Tuesday

The father emigrated thirty years ago to America. They have heard nothing of him since then.

The brother-in-law emigrated seven years ago. "What about your sister?" "My sister never speaks."

The father of the following one, who was a carabineer, was taken away as a spy by the Germans in 1943 because he had put up resistance in an alley-way. All the children have been brought up by the mother, his widow. "You admire your mother, don't you? She must have suffered."

"My mother is secretive. She never says anything."

Wednesday

"My father has tried to kill himself."

"How long ago . . . ?"

"The day before yesterday."

"The day before yesterday? I'm sorry . . ."

"Didn't you see about it in the paper?"

"Perhaps . . . I remember now . . . He threw himself from a window?"

"He threw himself from the third floor, from a balcony, but he wasn't killed. It's the second time he's tried; because he has a fixed idea that it's we who ought to have work. You see, Doctor, my sister, she has studied, and this has shaken her. She's more shaken than my father . . ."

"More than your father?"

"Doctor, I've come here also for my sister, to find work for her."

The fair-haired, delicate-looking young man is sure that after his father's attempt at suicide his sister will certainly be given work here.

Thursday

His brother was killed by a train. Why will they never use the level-crossing?

His brother was killed by a car on the high-road.

His brother had an illness as a child; which means that he is now an idiot. A girder fell on his father's back when he was working, causing an injury to the spine.

"How badly is he disabled?"

"Thirty per cent." No good to us: we have to take on a quota of disabled men, but disablement only of over forty per cent. Four more candidates. I try to hurry, out of sheer fatigue; but it is impossible, because even the most rapid talk implies a certain approach, a certain rhythm. I would like to make up my mind at once, but every time we have to go the same slow way about it. So one begins again:

"Where are you working now?"

"Nowhere. I'm unemployed."

"Where did you work?"

"At the engineering works, with the Allies. I was dismissed in '47, when the Allies went."

"And how do you spend your time now?"

"I do electrical repairs when I'm asked. I help in the house. I help my brother-in-law in the shop. I help my fiancée."

"What does your fiancée do?"

"She is a midwife." Another?

"I go out, I go for a walk with my friends. I read the sporting news. Sometimes a book, a thriller. I manage. I get along somehow."

A typical curriculum of certain southern workers would be as follows: Thirty years old. 1940-43: working on torpedoes. 1943: dismissed owing to the capitulation. Taken on later by the Allies for repair work on lorry engines, in the sheds of some industrial works destroyed by bombing. Dismissed by the Allies on their departure. 1948-50: policeman. 1950-52: employed on clerical work at the municipality of a small town in the interior. From 1952 on: unemployed.

Is he a clerical worker? Or a metal-worker? Or a policeman?

Now he is knocking again on the door of a factory, hoping to return to light mechanical work, which is what he started on; ready for a job at the assembly-lines, in the tool-room, or as a labourer. Ready to clean out the lavatories.

Some of the most moving cases are those of twenty-year-old youths, whose fathers are dead. They are the heads of their families, the only men, surrounded by six sisters and the mother.

I often see, during the interview, a man shaking his head at me in desperation.

CHAPTER XVI

Saturday

THE WORKERS AND clerical staff are continually stopping me on the stairs or in the workshops to recommend some relative who wants to be employed here. They ask for an interview with the Manager.

The social policy of our firm is to engage several members of the same family, in order that earnings should not become ineffective through dispersal. In this way it is hoped to form small, concentrated centres of prosperity that will indirectly be of benefit to other families too.

At Santa Maria, which is a reservoir of unemployment and under-employment, this system faces unpopularity and indignation. That the miracle of engagement by our factory should be found repeated two or three times in the same home instead of being more fairly distributed is hard to accept. Yet, if a doctor were to have two patients and one dose of a life-saving drug he would not halve it and let both patients die, but would give it all to one. This has been the line we have followed, at any rate up to the present time.

It has now been decided that relatives and dependents, instead of stopping me on the stairs, must write me a note and I will then send for them.

This is a new aspect of my work, which will really concern, at last, the interior of the factory, although on the face of it, it will still be a matter of dealing with those outside. But it is a reason for getting to know the workers and office staff better, and for having more serious talks with them.

I am always complaining to the Manager that my job is simply that of lightening the pressure from outside, of merely controlling the number of those who get through the entrance gates. The candidates appear before me and then disappear; and in seeing them so briefly, in not being able subsequently to follow them up, I feel that my part resembles that of an employee at a guichet, a confessor, a prostitute.

The machine-tools, despite the fact that they carry out minute and simple operations, repeated indefinitely, are very complex and work with great precision.

It is mysterious how the automatic lathes, in throwing off swarf, obey originally human commands that are now crystallized and impressed upon the machine. But the heart of all machinery is mysterious. Abstruse mathematical calculations control the disposition of the tools, and the angles at which the shavings are cut from the steel. Even the reading of the designs—the key to the mystery, the bridge between the mental image and its realization—is obscure to the layman, too.

The modern specialized worker may live beside his machine for years and use it with perfect accuracy, without understanding it. When something goes wrong, he calls in a mechanic more skilled than himself, such as a charge-hand. Then he goes on working it again, as though blindly. Unless he can get away and study the theory according to which they have been constructed, a man can handle machines all day and never know how they work. They simply go on turning automatically and, for him, miraculously. For months and years we hear the familiar bang, bang, of the big press—even from the garden, as one arrives, one is conscious of its throb, as though it were a symbol of the factory at work—but how do we think the die sets the strip of steel against the mould? How many people really know the true, mathematical working of the press?

Only the industrial experts and the engineers understand it. We humanists, and the workers themselves, will always be dominated by them and the obscurity by which their work is surrounded. We run the danger of thinking it all perfectly natural: the raw material, the machines, the ultimate aims of the factory. We stop asking ourselves the why and the wherefore, and accept everything as simple, eternal and immutable.

But better and more educated heads of departments are needed all the time to keep a factory up to date. For this reason our engineers have recently been running a course on Saturday afternoons to qualify our present apprentice charge-hands. This is held in the psychotechnical laboratory, which we clear for them on these half-days.

Our only Communist representative on the works committee attends this course; small, lively Amoruso, with his young face and grey hair. A good worker, diligent and reliable, he lives in one of the houses of our housing-estate and is full of self-esteem and pride in the factory.

This evening I met him as he was leaving the laboratory and I was going in to take possession of it once more. He looked tired and discouraged. The engineers had gone away. "Doctor, I'm thirty-five, and I'm no longer any good at book-work. My boy sees me in the evening with my exercise-books and my text-books under the lamp, just the same as him. Doctor, damn it all, haven't we earned any rights with all our practice and experience? Is it fair to send us back to school before giving us our qualifications?"

He was in a bad humour, because he had failed to understand a problem set out on the blackboard; usually so wide-awake, he had been sleepy that afternoon. It would seem that his Marxism makes him regard Saturday schooling in a worse light than ignorance: inciting him the more against a class that allows the workers to be uneducated and then, when they become fathers of families, tries to turn them into trained men.

Monday

Donnarumma has refused a subsidy from the management, offered him through the medium of the officer of Carabineers, who has to see him over the matter of our denunciation; not that he did not know him already.

He was offered the subsidy in the hope of pricking the black, swollen blister of his wrath; and because, despite a warning from the police that he was not again to set foot in the porters' lodge, he leaves the wall, crosses the road and prowls along the windows of the laboratory. The officer himself advised a subsidy rather than another complaint on our part; a pacific gesture, he thought, might be a good thing, and even free us perhaps from his presence.

In refusing, Donnarumma insists on a fixed indemnity of forty thousand *lire* a month for wrongful dismissal as a labourer.

As is usual now between us and Donnarumma, the negotiation went through and came to nothing without any contact between us.

Yesterday evening, Sunday, an evening of still almost summer warmth, there was a grand *festa* in inauguration of the figure of the Madonna that, at the desire of the inhabitants, is to watch over our factory housing-estate. The votive figure, in a blue cloak embellished with gold stars, stands in a small chapel of abstract design, consisting of two sheets of glass placed at an angle. This is the work of one of our geometricians, and is an expression of the meeting-point between modern industrial rationalism and the ancient religious beliefs.

I missed the religious ceremony and the fireworks, and I arrived just as a crowd of friends and relations were departing across the mown lawns of the village and the small, closed piazza with its colour-washed houses. They were quietly leaving the illuminated Madonna, after saying their prayers. It was a very clear night, and from the windows and balconies of these houses, lit up by the lamps within, the neighbours were calling to one another. As we hoped, they are already re-creating, under a modern welfare economy, the life of the alley-ways and court-yards of the old towns.

I thought I had missed the whole thing. But instead, a more intimate *festa* was just beginning. The organizing committee, the works com-mittee and the management met in Amoruso's house, one of the largest and best-furnished in the village, to which they had been at once invited by the host himself.

The others, management and staff, were sitting against the white walls of the room, some with their wives, whom we met for the first time, two or three with children. The engineers were there, the doctor, the Signorina from the social welfare office, Straniero and the members of the works committee, and men from the workshops. There were not very many of us, nor any unfamiliar faces, but it seemed odd to us to be meeting in a private house.

Cakes and vermouth were handed round. A photographer took some of the groups: all of one sort, when he got the wives together on the sofa, or three of the managerial staff sitting talking to one another; but afterwards he decided boldly to mix workers, clerks, wives and engineers together for some final records of the *festa*.

Amoruso, who seemed to have recovered his equanimity, introduced his wife and children to me, all smartly dressed, together with the small boy who studies with him in the evenings. His wife was the only worker's wife present; neither Straniero nor any of the others had brought theirs.

The conversation was cheerful in tone, very friendly and a little flat, as is usual among people who are mutually attached, but, though amused at meeting on a social footing have nothing new to say to one another. The children made most noise, playing in the limited space available among the chairs and the guests' legs. Finally, after several vermouths, one saw at the other end of the room, outside the circle of chairs, the president of the organizing committee, a young man from the assembly-lines, climb on to Amoruso's dining-table for the toasts. Whereas at first we had been all together, he had now taken his friends the workers with him and they were grouped around the table. "To the health of the organizing committee which . . . which . . ." he began, red in the face and with his hair standing on end. "To the health of the organizing committee which . . . which . . ." and got down again among his friends. Then he climbed back on to the table, gave a toast, and got down. He climbed up again. We watched him benevolently; the Manager laughed out loud. But perhaps it was the moment, at least for us, to bring the *festa* to an end.

Again we found ourselves on the little piazza, which was still illuminated by fairy lights slung from the lamp-standards and the open windows. There was waste-paper and rubbish on the grass and on the geometrically planned stone paths; but tomorrow the cleaning squad would put all that to rights, thus checking at once any danger of renascent untidiness.

On my way from Amoruso's house to the high-road I was greeted by many people. In the dark I could hardly see them, and responded gaily, under the influence of the *festa* and its air of harmony. I thought I knew or recognized them all. One after the other, two men, appearing out of the night, introduced themselves as relations of workers of ours and said that the Manager had promised each of them an interview this week. I returned home having greatly enjoyed myself, with my pockets full of requests for work.

Today the Manager told me that he had not spoken a word to any-one on the subject of work.

These autumn days must be particularly propitious for religious celebrations and processions. Since the day before yesterday loud-speakers of the Holy Mission have been sounding in the streets of Castello, exhorting the people to prayer.

Prayers, exhortations and warnings resound among the fumes from the steel-works, and spread up from the coast over the whole hillside, reaching even my house. Every evening when I return, this preparation for the Last Judgment, this apocalyptic Mission, fills the air and the sky with its message. The priests sweep through the streets quarter by quarter, with women and children at their heels; gathering them up from the pavements and the doorways in an increasing crowd until they reach one of the churches of Castello.

Alternating with the traditional prayers, all the slogans of redemp-tion for the workers are launched on the streets and in the pagan out-skirts of the city. In the silence of the country one can just hear the distant voices: "Christ is passing among you, men of the steel-works, among you . . . Pater Noster . . ." It is the thunderous voice of a priest; in going about Castello, concerned to all appearance with the souls of the women and children, the Holy Mission is in reality aiming its shafts at the Red stronghold of the steel-works.

"Men of the steel-works . . . beware of forgetting . . . of forgetting . . . Christ. Tomorrow the Holy Mission . . . five-thirty . . . your hearts . . . your wives . . . your sins . . ." In the garden, a gust of wind is enough to break the thread of the appeals, and one only hears a toneless booming sound. Then, suddenly, the loudspeaker comes through again: "Your hearts do not bleed . . . Tomorrow at five-thirty . . ."

Although they are invisible from my terrace one hears them winding their way through Castello, round the walls of the steel-works, under the light of the roadside lamps. The darker it grows, the louder seems the tramp of the feet of the faithful and the hoots of the loudspeakers, carried by the wind from the sea. And so the Mission noisily passes on its way, far from my house and the factory, in the silence of the night.

CHAPTER XVII

Monday

We have been reduced to asking for a carabineer at our doors. And I have suspended my interviews with the workers who want their relatives to be given jobs here. I had to give up. The task has been taken over by the Manager.

If I explained to one of our men that his brother had failed in the tests, he either immediately proposed another brother or accused me of deliberately making trouble; if I told another that there were hopes for him, he went at once to the works committee to ask if I were not "pulling his leg". Not all the interviews went like this; but all dragged out their length for about an hour and lost their way in a fog of demands and excuses. One worker threatened suicide at my table, and another, from the presses, held me personally responsible for the engagement—entirely fictitious—of three brothers of one of his mates. Placing their hopes in my sympathetic nature they were spurred on to stress their need with ever greater insistence. It is over now; Operation Internal Relations is ended, wrecked by this question of the relatives. The Manager will deal with it from behind his more authoritative desk.

This morning I thought that Attanasio, one of the men from the workshop, had come to my room on behalf of some relative of his, either because he did not know of the change or because he was unwilling to face the Manager.

Attanasio has a very big chin and a crooked nose. "Listen, Attanasio," I began, "about your sister . . ." He sat down wearily and, shaking his head, said:

"They tell me that you are a psychologist and understand . . ."

"I understand, but your sister . . . the Manager himself will arrange about her."

"No, I mean that you understand the workers here. I have a fixed idea." He hung his head. "I am worn out." So he had come to see me about himself.

"Do you find the work at the benches hard? You can tell me about it. Does it get on your nerves?"

"I'm done up. Not because of the work. I have this fixed idea. You must give me the address of a psycho-analyst."

"But there are no psycho-analysts in the city here."

I mastered my astonishment, and, assuming an air of unconcern, waited for him to go on. He dropped his eyes in embarrassment and continued to waste time.

"What fixed idea, Attanasio?" I asked quietly. "There are very few psycho-analysts in Italy, and those there are . . . It's a highly skilled profession. They are paid at least three thousand *lire* for each consultation, and if the treatment is to be successful one has to go over and over again . . ."

"Three thousand *lire*? And how many times?"

"Three times a week. A minimum of six months. Three multiplied by three make . . ." Attanasio seemed to have relapsed into indifference. Yet it might be that his crooked face was deceptive and it was really the indifference of despair. He repeated: "I have this fixation."

"Have you had it long?"

"For a month." Either he must be made to reveal his obsession or I should have to acknowledge my first defeat—after the fiasco of the relatives—in the factory's internal welfare relations. "I am not a psychoanalyst, but I know the . . . I know the problems, I can help you. And then, I cost nothing!"

He did not smile; indeed, he became more sombre and reserved than ever, looking vaguely about him. Finally, he caught my eye and said: "For the last month I've been impotent."

"Well now, tell me about it . . ."

"For a month I've had a new girl, but when I have connection with her I find I'm no good," he said in a toneless voice.

"It's not a serious matter." Yet he, too, seemed to regard it as tiresome rather than grave. "Has it ever happened to you before?"

"No. Before, I used to go with a married woman. She meant nothing to me. But I had no difficulty with her."

"It's perfectly natural. The fact that with the married woman . . . that is, the fact that you didn't care for her caused you to become . . ." I was speaking in a low voice, as I always did in my office, but all the same I rose and closed the door between my room and that of the Signorina, who at the moment was not using her typewriter, but quietly reading. I came back and sat down, giving my patient's aggressive chin a glance as I did so . . . "caused you to have full, complete satisfaction with her."

Half convinced, the patient nodded and said in a detached way: "I didn't care a damn for the married woman."

"Weren't you even afraid of the husband? Because fear, as is well known, can produce this condition."

"I was never afraid of her husband," retorted the seducer, truculently. "Women, for me, have always been like shirts, to throw aside when soiled."

"Instead, this time you're in love?" I asked, somewhat ironically.

"Yes, I love the girl, although she's not a virgin."

"Ah, she's not a virgin?"

"She says I'm frigid."

"What a mistake!" Beneath this mask of a seducer there might lie real desperation, leading to a fall in his output at the benches. "How wrong she is," I went on sympathetically. "You must tell her that it is just your love for her that causes this condition. Medical science explains it as produced by a state of emotional tension, of excessive excitement or apprehension, due to too intense feeling . . ."

He listened gloomily, but did not react to the argument of an excess of love; perhaps this girl, too, was a shirt to be discarded? Perhaps his condition would persist, and, owing to a mistaken diagnosis, we should lose the only worker who had ever come to consult the psychologist on his own behalf.

"You can always go and see the factory doctor and speak quite freely to him, as to me. More freely than to me . . ." I saw that I should have to touch on aspects of a more physiological kind.

"I've been to him. He says it will pass."

"He didn't find you exhausted in any way?"

"No."

"Well then, since you are here, let us go into another aspect of the matter: one which psychology takes into account. How do you have your contacts with this girl?"

"In her house. Or we go out."

"Does she live alone?"

"She has her father and mother with her, and five brothers. And a grandmother. I go there when she's alone."

"When she's alone? You have to be quick, presumably . . ."

"Two or three minutes."

"There, you see, it's pretty hurried . . . This haste, and the fear of being found by her father, would naturally affect your nervous sensibility. And then, too, when you are out together—you can never be sure of not being disturbed. At Santa Maria, with so many people about . . . There must be very few quiet places. Where do you go?"

"Yes, there are very few. We walk along the sea, beyond the baths . . ."

Beyond the Roman baths there is a piece of rocky coast that is more or less deserted, but within a yard or two of the railway-line with its passing trains. Nearer the sea the rocks are full of children.

The conversation languished; Attanasio was brooding again on his love-affair with an anxiety that seemed emphasized by his chin.

"How often?" I asked sharply.

"How do you mean?"

"How many times a week?" As I spoke, the Signorina came in for a moment to look for some papers in the files; he took no notice of her and indeed was bent on replying. I did not want him to regard the subject of our talk as in any way clandestine, or rather, I did not want to instil in him a sense of guilt; and I was forced to fill the moments until the Signorina's exit with hasty, non-committal explanations:

"It will be all right. You must come back whenever you like and tell me how things are going. And, with the person in question, use the argument that I have just put before you. It is the best line to take . . ." The Signorina caught my eye with a knowing glance, convinced that the man was complaining of his foreman or one of the engineers: and that I was embarrassed, as usual, when trouble arose between different ranks in the factory. As soon as she had left, I asked again:

"How many times a week?"

"Every day."

"But when?"

"After work."

"Isn't it too much?"

"With the married woman I did it twice a day for a year."

"Try to space it out."

"It's not possible." We fell silent, and he became glum, discontented, again.

"It never happened before, never. With the married woman . . ."

"Yes, yes, I understand. Listen, I guarantee that there is not the very least loss of your virility. On the contrary!"

For the first time he smiled.

"And then—I don't want you to enter into details now—but one must consider the situations, the . . . positions."

Still serious, he began his explanation: "Very often, standing . . ."

"Then no wonder!" I exclaimed.

"She thinks I am frigid. She complains. Yesterday evening she said so again. And I'm not frigid."

"You were on the beach?"

"At her house. Not on the bed. On a chair."

"But in three minutes . . . You must explain to the girl, it's the very reverse of frigidity. Women understand, intuitively. This is a passing phase. It's the proof of your love, of the fact that this relationship is of importance to you, it's the proof that you want to marry her. The girl should be glad of it."

"No, she complains. Before, with the others, I just used them like shirts."

"Yes, soiled shirts. But this one is not a shirt. She is a wife." I had to end the interview.

But then I hesitated, and tried once more to convince him, to insert into his mind the germs of recovery, despite his air of a disgruntled seducer. So in the end, still surly, he took his leave, and without showing the relief or gratitude of one who has had a weight removed from his mind, set off for the workshop, without even the hint of a smile: dejected, but to some extent mollified.

We are hoping that by now Paola Alemanno is married. During the last month she has failed to reach the altar, the ceremony having been twice postponed.

Since the man she is to marry lives a long way off, she will have to give up her place at the machine-testing; but since she was the only member of her family in work we had to replace her either by a brother or a sister, or otherwise she would never have abandoned her family for another. During the last few weeks she has been to see me and the Manager six times to recommend a brother or sister, as the date of her marriage inexorably approached; each time the intervening period was shorter and it became more and more urgent to effect the exchange.

We wanted to help the girl and not to force her to give up her marriage. But her brother, a bewildered slip of a boy, dreamy as all the other Alemmanos are, was simply not old enough: we should have had to reopen the case of the Chiodo boy, had we engaged him. Whereas Paola, although she is so essentially feminine, has spirit and determination; she has shown this in her work and is giving proof of it now, in her defence of the only wages earned in her family; ready even to run the risk of sacrificing herself.

Last Tuesday she came to propose her sister. She was sobbing, because the wedding was to be on Saturday. I told her to bring the girl to see me.

I already knew that they would not have her at the machine-testing. An engineer and a charge-hand had seen her, and found her a girl of feeble physique. But I told Paola to bring her along, because I knew that the Manager intended to help her even against the decision of the technical experts.

Both girls, of thin and delicate appearance, came to see me in the afternoon. Paola had had two years of heavy work at the testing; she had not missed a day. All the preparations for her wedding were before her; she still had to iron her trousseau herself. She was sobbing as one with a right to escape. Instead, the sister, who resembled her, but was shorter and even thinner, seemed absent-minded as, wearing a cardigan, she stood beside Paola in her white working overall.

I guaranteed the exchange at once. Paola smiled, and her eyes shone with joy through the tears on her lashes. However, owing to the opposition, well justified as it was, of the technicians, I could not guarantee Caterina a place at the machine-testing.

"You can start work tomorrow morning. You will begin by doing cleaning or by attending in the sick-room. If you do well, you will go on to the machine-testing, like your sister."

She shook her head without a word, as though faced by an impossibility. Cleaning or work in the sick-room would dishonour her. And Paola, after a moment, was with her and against me. "I'll give up my marriage. I'll give it up."

"She must begin with the cleaning and then we'll see. She must show how well she works. In the meantime you can marry; listen, Alemanno, you can't postpone your wedding again. And what for? For a foolish idea you have got into your head."

"I want to take on her job, only her job," whispered the sister. Paola felt extreme remorse at sacrificing her, and clasped her trembling hands together. For her too the dishonour of doing cleaning work ruined everything.

"Listen, Alemanno, go back to your place. I'll speak to your sister. Go back to the machine-testing." I repeated the order so firmly that she obediently turned and went, without a glance behind her, and I was left alone with the other.

"Are you jealous of your sister?"

"No, no."

"Why don't you want her to marry, then?"

"I want her to marry."

"What did you say?" She was barely audible.

"I do want her to marry." At last she seemed to pull herself together, and dried her eyes.

"If you refuse to come and work here, you can't want her to marry."

"But I want to work as she did."

"And how did she work?"

"I don't know, Doctor, seated of course . . ." she said, her voice fading away again, as she wriggled like a cat.

"She worked as everyone works here. Everyone is equal."

"But I don't want to do cleaning, I can't . . ."

"Why?"

"I'm afraid."

"Are you afraid of cleaning? Or perhaps you are afraid of the work in the sick-room, the injections?"

"Doctor . . . a girl . . . It's looked down on. A girl who does cleaning never finds a husband."

"Your sister has found a husband because she works sitting down?" She smiled.

"A worker at the machine-testing, a worker who does the cleaning, it's all the same," I said quickly. She didn't follow me, and I had to think of something to secure her attention.

"My parents wouldn't like it, either, Doctor. One goes about all day, everyone would see me."

"And what would they see?" She smiled; now she understood.

"What on earth would they see?" I laughed, and she was quick to seize the opportunity.

"They would see that I only did cleaning, while the others were sitting down. No one here would do domestic work . . . cleaning. How do you think the men here would treat them?"

"You are mistaken. Do get it into your head that all the work is on an equality here: do you understand? No one in this factory is allowed to think that some do honourable work and others what is degrading. Go and tell your friends that there are no differences of that sort here. We don't allow the men and women who do the cleaning, or the nurses, to be looked down on by the others. We don't allow it! The only difference lies between those who have the will to work and those who haven't." I leant towards her as I spoke, reasonably and rapidly, at first with a paternal air, then almost hissing at her.

She drew back, her face grown expressionless with fear.

"Do you understand? Come tomorrow morning. We will expect

you." She seemed to agree, and made an almost flirtatious grimace.

"You have your sister's happiness in your hands. Your sister deserves all you can give her. She has always been most courageous . . ."

"Yes, Doctor." She was overwhelmed by the scolding she had had from me. Without realizing it I had put the egalitarian code of the factory and the idea of female emancipation in the balance against the slight body and slow wits of the younger Alemanno.

"We'll expect you tomorrow. Your sister's happiness is in your hands, and it depends on you whether the personnel office is put to shame or not."

The contrast between her responsibility and her limited intelligence, between this new, heavy burden and the slender strength of her arms, chest and back, seemed greater than ever. She left as though blown by a breath of air that might or might not blow her here again tomorrow.

That evening Paola Alemanno pulled the levers of the calculators for the last time. She knew of the agreement with her sister. The relief of this decision could be seen in her bowed head as one passed behind her, and her eyes, which looked nowhere in search of distraction. They looked within her.

Caterina did not appear next morning. The Signorina and I awaited her anxiously, and had to warn the cleaning department that she was missing. We waited till mid-day: perhaps she was only late. By mid-day there was still no sign of either of them. The personnel office had clearly made a mistake in trusting to the word of a prejudiced young girl, without principles or conscience. We had been carried away by our individual sympathies.

If she did not present herself at two in the afternoon, Caterina's job would have gone for good, and we should have proof of the fact that by showing too much pity in one case one may be unfair towards others: for hundreds of women in Santa Maria would have gladly replaced the girl who left to be married. We would have to abandon the Alemanno family to their own devices. The Signorina, however, said to me in her brusque way: "Please, drive me down to their house to see what has happened. It's not far, I know how to find it."

We set off in the lunch-hour, towards Grotte.

The little seaside town was empty of visitors, the season being over. Only two slowly moving cars, and a few permanently unemployed men, were to be seen on the road under the pines. A group of our applicants were sitting outside a café, and I endeavoured not to be seen as we passed.

At the crossroads we took the turning leading towards the dark,

wooded lake inland, and skirted the other lake by the coast with its
plantations of canes. The Spanish castle, with its crooked lines and
pale colouring, dominated the sea. We stopped at the first house
after the lake, a square, grey and white, isolated cottage, enclosed in a
small field between the sea and a reed-bed. The Signorina got out at
once and taking the path to the house, went up the broken steps of a
stairway leading from the ground to the first and only floor, while I
slowly followed her. She went up so confidently that one might have
thought her intimately acquainted with the house, and knocked, but
there was no reply. Pushing open the door, she went in. No one
appeared on the path or from the reed-bed, and I remained waiting at
the foot of the steps. One might well ask oneself if such an expedition
were justified, or whether it formed part of the duties of the office.
Luckily, no one passed on the road, and we were unseen, surrounded
by the silence of the country and the sea, which was almost as smooth
as the lake.

After a few minutes the Signorina looked out. I had not heard them
speaking distinctly, partly because I had not listened, and had maintained a somewhat official attitude below the stairway. She said:
"They are alone here, in bed. Both together, crying, in one another's
arms." She turned back at once, leaving the door ajar.

I could not hear them crying, but the Signorina's firm voice reached
me, and it was then that I looked through the door and saw in the
darkness a big, white bed under a glimmering lamp in the middle of
the room. The shutters were closed. As one of the girls emerged from
the bedclothes and went to open the window, I withdrew.

I went back to the car, and after ten minutes or so the Signorina
came down the steps holding the little Alemanno girl by the hand.
Her pale cheeks were blotched with red and she wore her blue cardigan
as on the previous day, with a tight black skirt gripping her thin thighs.
We put her in the back of the car and set off immediately.

"I told Paola to get ready for her wedding. I made this one dress at
once and come to the factory."

"Was no one there?"

"They were alone, in bed. They had wept all night. Paola had
decided not to marry."

"But her sister persuaded her?"

"I had to persuade the sister too."

"Still against the cleaning?"

"The cleaning, and the sick-room. She didn't want to become a
domestic servant."

Caterina, bent double in the back seat of the little car, was silent but her head was close to ours. "What silly nonsense," I said, loudly, on purpose. "But how about the others of the family?"

"The head of the family is Paola. What will happen now that she is going away . . ."

"They'll see now what they owe her."

"She was elder sister, mother and father in one."

"They'll know now."

"She supported the whole house."

"They exploited her. The others don't know their duty. They'll understand now." Caterina made no movement, and spoke no word.

Once more we went through Grotte, empty except for two bicyclists and a cart, and made straight for the factory.

A group of men were standing at the porters' lodge: some of our workers perhaps, who had gone down into the roadway after lunch. No. They were not wearing overalls. They were the same lot.

I saw Chiodo first, with his usual appendage of a son; then Papaleo. Finally, Donnarumma, Dattilo and Accettura, among others who were unknown to me, and included a broad-shouldered young man in a fisherman's jersey, who for some days had been demanding, with a newcomer's energy, not only a job in the factory but medicine for his ill child. He, too, like Accettura, lived in a cave below the high-road.

He was the first to make a move towards the car. I had to slow down, because they were deliberately surrounding us. "Put on speed, get through quickly," said the Signorina. Assisted by Santoro, Bellomo succeeded in clearing a way for us. I was still slowing down, struck not so much by the danger of hitting someone as by the familiar faces: Papa's big one looming behind my window, with his close-set green eyes, his wrinkles and the hair hiding his wound; and a fleeting glimpse of Donnarumma's sinister visage. "They're the usual lot," exclaimed the Signorina. "What are they doing here? Do they still not understand? Go on, go on. Don't slow up."

I accelerated, and Caterina, crouching under the hood of the car, was jerked backwards, hitting her head. We brushed past Chiodo's son, who was given a push towards me by his father, and, obeying Bellomo's gesticulations, shot up the now empty drive. They could not follow us there.

Since it was after one o'clock, the portico at the top was fortunately now empty; the lunch-break was over, the beat of the press could again be heard, and the factory was at work. We extracted the little Alemanno from her corner and the Signorina hurried her inside; if she were

made ready at once and in secret, perhaps the engineers would not
notice her absence of half a day.

Having parked my car under the portico, I went down again
to the porters' lodge on foot. Beyond the wall of the factory, the
horizon was filled with an opaque-coloured sea, which in the early
afternoon has a grey, deserted look. There was no one to be seen
about the drive.

I wondered if the men had gathered at the entrance simply because
they had seen us leave the gates, or whether some grapevine message
had reported that we had been at Grotte; in any case, it was time someone went to give Bellomo some moral support.

In fact, Bellomo and Santoro, outside the cabin, were almost weeping with impotent rage. But they had broken up the group, and driven
them from the gates. Along the wall on the other side of the road were
ranged our old disreputable acquaintances, Chiodo and his son, Donnarumma and Papa, with some others. "We drove them off," said
Bellomo, vehemently, "and now they're over there. But, Doctor,"
he added, with dignity, "they give too much trouble." The new
applicants, who always have a right to wait, were now gathering
under the covered way, with others, pacific but inveterate loiterers at
our gate; Dattilo among them, sadly contemplating the ground with a
lost and guilty air.

I looked at the field of battle, as I stood at Bellomo's side.

From the edge of the pavement opposite, the routed forces were
making a show of broaching the asphalt of the roadway; they stepped
on to it and then withdrew, put a foot forward and took it back,
for all the world as though they were playing at Tom Tiddler's
Ground. In revenge for their defeat, they were jeering at our guards.
It was all Bellomo and Santoro could do not to go for them once more.
Papa was vaguely waving an arm.

"Look at him, Doctor," said Bellomo, in a strangled voice.

"Leave him alone, he won't do anything."

I walked back under the covered way, among the others, and within
a stone's throw of the group of scoffers on the other side of the road.
They were not aiming at me, however, but at their fellow-townsmen
our guards, who, in their view, considered themselves superior because
they wore peaked caps on their heads. I wanted to show that the
situation was perfectly quiet and I also wanted to give Bellomo all the
moral backing he needed.

I walked slowly from one end of the covered way to the other,
among the parked cars and motor bicycles, brushing past the group of

men with whom, for the moment, one had no fault to find except for their absurd insistence on waiting here indefinitely. I expected every minute that they would surround me to ask questions.

Instead, they were discussing something among themselves. They had gathered round a man, unknown to me, thin and with a narrow head, who, for a moment, I thought was Accettura, for he rather resembled him. Instead, Accettura had joined the reprobates on the other side of the road; in any case, this newcomer, though extremely shabbily dressed, was evidently endowed with a facile tongue, for he was haranguing the rest with insolent ease.

They were attending to him, not to me. New and old, Dattilo too, and the hot-tempered fisherman whose baby was ill, were all listening to him. None of them noticed me, although I almost touched them in passing. I turned back, and passed them again, but not a head turned in my direction.

Finding themselves within our inviolable walls, and, for the moment, left in peace, they were being addressed by one of themselves: with the air of those who, having lost all hope, and with it, respect and fear, they were, in the most natural manner conceivable, treating the place as though it were their own.

"Do you know why it is that this factory is no longer taking on men?" shouted the newcomer. I passed behind Dattilo's back, but, like all the rest, he was too fascinated by the speaker to notice me.

"Do you know why they are taking on no more men? Because they are only engaging women."

The orator then asked himself a rhetorical question: "And why are they only taking women?" He was speaking for all those who were there listening to him, employed and unemployed, and he replied to his own question: "Because the engineers . . . them."

His hearers were not really convinced; they did not laugh, but muttered, doubtfully. The group began to break up, and they wandered off, their hands in their pockets. There was nothing to say to them, because whether they believed the accusation or not, they felt, for the moment, free, and they would allow no one the privilege of contradicting or intimidating them.

In the Manager's spacious office that afternoon we again discussed whether to call in the police for a second time to deal with Donnarumma: the evidence was that it was he who had organized the attempt on my car, but after it had been surrounded, events had taken a different turn and had escaped his control.

Donnarumma had not made his move on account of our abduction

of Caterina Alemanno, but because, having seen the Signorina and
me go off in the direction of Grotte, he had deduced that we would
not be long in returning: he therefore gathered the rest of them—
always hanging round the vicinity of the factory—and worked them
up with his incoherent phrases. "He was baying like a mongrel
hound," declared Bellomo. "Like a mongrel hound. You ought to
arm us with revolvers."

A second denunciation to the police would send Donnarumma to
prison; without one, the position of our guards would be weakened.

We therefore decided to take a middle course and to ask for a
carabineer to be stationed at the entrance.

CHAPTER XVIII

Thursday

THE SOLITARY CARABINEER standing outside our gates, on the now cleared threshold of the porters' lodge, looks impressive, but his presence would seem to be useless, and he himself is bored at having nothing to do; perhaps, before long, he too will be asking to enter.

Both we and the engineering works now have carabineers at our doors: we because we are engaging workers and they because they are dismissing theirs.

Have we been wrong in our policy? Have we been too weak, or too strict? But in the factory, work goes on tranquilly. Little by little more men have been taken on, and the empty spaces in the workshops have all been filled up. The assembly-lines are crowded. I no longer know every name and every face. Even Ugo has become merged with his companions; his former history, and the mornings when he came to wring our hearts, have now faded. His fingers tremble less and less. Ugo's future history is now laid down for him, as it is for all the others; it will have its ups and downs, but they will be those of a worker's life.

The personnel office of tomorrow will be hard put to it to re-discover these people now absorbed into the ferment of work that fills this long room, packed with benches; or to carry out investigations in the productive, civilized community of the workshops, which becomes more and more anonymous. Individual adventures will come to an end, and the day of a worker's engagement will no longer be the one critical day of his life, a day of birth. From under the stratification of months and years of work in the factory, the personnel office will have to dig individuals out to ensure that all goes well with them; it will have to find a system for knowing and understanding them, even without remembering all their names.

When that day comes, my successor will have more time at his disposal, because the inflow at the porters' lodge will be stopped; but the workers will have assumed a more collective face, and one more to be feared.

I shall go down in the factory's history as the man of the porters' lodge. Now that the carabineer blocks the flood-gates and the factory's waters are under control, I am being transferred. I am leaving.

No one, as yet, except the Manager, knows this. Dattilo, for instance, still puts his hopes in me for next winter, having always given proof of good behaviour. He is convinced that I will reward him, and that my wife must, surely, say a word in favour of his wife.

Even if one would like to stay here for ever, one's career, one's destiny, leads one inevitably back to the centre, to the cities of the north.

Perhaps the factory during these recent times has been becoming too much of a home. Its political significance as an experiment carried out in southern Italy—the opening up, by a modern industry, of new industrial life—has been losing interest for me, caught up, as I have been, in the daily round. The autumn sunsets are still streaking the sky at twilight with tongues of flame and scarlet behind the island, in unchanging glory. It is dangerous to become infected with love for one particular factory.

Saturday

Love of a factory is the inevitable human love for, and pride in, one's work and the character of an individual firm; but it also means renunciation of a wider life. Pride in one's firm may be a refuge from a society in which one has no faith; for which one no longer has hopes.

Naturally, my departure is not taking place at once, but in a few weeks' time, and I shall continue here meanwhile as though I were not going. Work makes one forget, and then, one evening, having cleared everything up, one leaves as usual, and the only difference is that next morning one does not return.

Some of our workers are asking to be transferred to the clerical staff, because of their former schooling. It was to be expected. But on these occasions the engineers repent their own weakness in being influenced by the unfortunate situation of students—left without resources halfway through the secondary school or university—and of having dangled before them the possibility of earning technical diplomas. And again, it is on these occasions that the solid figure of the traditional proletarian returns to its own. Fortunately, the list of those who think themselves unadapted to their present work does not include the ex-secondary schoolboy from the assembly-lines: either he has become wholly absorbed into the life of a worker, or he is keeping silent.

Taronna, on the other hand, who previously had done three years of accountancy and knows one foreign language—the most insistent, the most impatient of his working overalls—has been relegated permanently to the workshops: a bad worker does not merit promotion. He was basing his hopes of rising just on this fact of being a bad worker, in proof of his superior aptitudes.

Monday

In the tool-room, the new fitters have been doing their test-pieces, the sum of their skill and experience, in six, eight or fourteen hours. They were making hexagonal or dove-tailed grooves in a block of steel, and with great accuracy cutting out hexagons or dove-tailed pieces to fit into them.

During the test they mix with the real fitters on the benches and at the machines, but one can soon pick them out by some flurried movement, and the anxiety with which they use their tools. One of them lets his file drop and picks it up as though he thinks it about to be stolen from him; and they run from the bench to the drill and back to the bench again. The difficulty and fatigue of the work are such that one cannot help wishing they had some easier material to deal with: if it were only plasticine or wax . . . With the adamantine quality of steel, one stroke too many with the file and the piece is ruined, no miracle can add a millimetre to it.

Ripamonti, like a good teacher, gathers them on an uncrowded bench and furnishes them with every tool that will help them to conquer their initial nervousness; but once they begin he watches them secretly, without pity. More and more, as the day goes on, they behave like the others, and seem to work as they do; but in fact they still stand out as though surrounded by an aura of nervous excitement.

Ripamonti was tossing a dove-tail made yesterday from one hand to another; he indicated with a shocked air that there was an imperceptible gap at a corner, a 'tolerance' that the department would not dream of accepting: the steel must fit as though the cut had not been made and the material were again a single piece. A chink of some tenth of a millimetre is in Ripamonti's eyes a dangerous abyss that is quite enough to condemn its guilty author.

When the masterpiece is a success, it is my job to give an interview to check up on the trainee; but who would dare reject the maker of a perfect join, an invisible scar? The candidate would at least have to show signs of madness or moral obliquity combined with his technical skill. These interviews are conducted with an air of respect for the achievement that endows the man beyond my table with glory; for if, after he had produced a perfect dove-tail by unerring strokes of the file, I were to reject the artist, I should no longer be received by Ripamonti with honour in his department.

Leaving the tool-room, I passed Attanasio, who was sitting absorbed in his work at the benches, at three removes from Bonocore. He seemed neither gloomy nor cheerful, and gave me a grave nod of the head in salutation, without smiling. He has not been back to the personnel office and his psychological treatment has therefore lapsed. Either he must have recovered or he has lost faith in the mind doctor; in any case, he is doing without my help, and therefore I cannot ask him how things are going, though I should like to do so.

Thursday

New models are being put into production, and the assembly lines are becoming more crowded than ever.

With the new work-stages, it is taking longer for the men to reach piece-work rates, because they have to learn the whole stage from the beginning, and try it out again and again. At the assembly-lines the best workers are put on to the new products, men who, on the old lines, were earning the highest rates. As a reward they are being given this change of job which means that for some weeks they will be earning less.

There are moments in which the piece-work system, which is a progressive conquest, stands revealed in its slave-driving aspect. It rewards the best workers, it keeps discipline by replacing the lash, and repays labour with gain; but it makes the worker a slave to time and to his pay, and causes him to be valued for what he can do rather than for what he is. This is, in fact, where he becomes cut off from the life outside. One day it will disappear, when the worker has a right to a fixed wage, and the incentive of piece-work is no longer held to be necessary. The worker will work on his own, with no need of the lash, his conscience and his interests coinciding.

Glancing through a news-sheet in the office, the Signorina reads an article on the decadence of the bicycle. The bicycle factories, even in the north, are in a state of crisis; however—observes the impartial writer of the article—"in northern Italy the Atala and Ligie firms are able to carry on because they depend for workers on the inmates of the prisons of Padua and Verona, and therefore their labour costs are extremely low".

Friday

The private agent, the influential inhabitant of Santa Maria, who has remained something of a phantom because no one has ever revealed his name, has not given a sign of life for a long time. Yesterday he again caught a woman with his bait, and this morning she came here. She asserted that the man was, in the last century, godfather to our President's father, that is, to the founder of the firm, and that for this reason he had great influence over our choice of personnel.

One of the workers, named Di Marzo, has been designated by the doctor as suffering from a "non-physical" complaint, and must be watched.

Caterina Alemanno has been sent to the factory housing estate; she has the garden to weed, and some premises used for club and cultural purposes to clean. During the day there are only women and children about the village and Caterina, as she wished, is not subjected to the glances of the men while at her work.

But now she is bored, and walks sadly about the garden. She complains to the Signorina that we have left her to work too much alone.

Friday afternoon

Coffee is not drunk in the factory, and there is no near-by bar. Only the Manager possesses a coffee-machine and two small cups in his private washplace, of which his secretary has charge; in the workshops they have started the distribution of soft drinks, but not coffee.

When, halfway through the afternoon, it is no longer possible to resist the longing for coffee, members of the staff who have cars slip away to the bar at Grotte.

For some weeks, however, I have not frequented Grotte or Castello because of Donnarumma. I have completely abandoned Santa Maria, and have almost forgotten that most beautiful inferno, with its steep roads down to the centre, its crowded piazza and public garden: our overflowing reservoir of workers who emerge from it in the morning and drift back at night. It is my fate now to see it through their talk, as though it were a city unknown to me, as in my early days here.

In the long, lazy, still hot afternoon, my fear of Donnarumma was today overcome by this attraction of the bar at Grotte, where, from the factory, one drops right down to sea-level. A sense of perpetual, out-of-season idleness and boredom reigns in the small empty piazzetta, shaded by its pines and olive trees. This is the solitary south, with just a few men to watch the time go by. The fresh, soft air cools early in the afternoon, because the sun sinks behind the high crest of a hill overhanging the village.

Such men as there are in the place scrape a living somehow; they go to and fro between the deserted bathing-beach and one or two shops that sell fruit, groceries and tobacco.

A tinkling cane curtain at the door of the bar moved as I entered, and set up a buzz of flies, now that October is ending. Five unemployed men were playing billards and did not look up.

Our fisherman applicant with the discoloured jersey and the thick neck of an ex-boxer was leaning on the bar, but not eating or drinking. It was thus that I fell in with Dongiovanni, for all the world as though he were waiting for me. The coffee was slow in appearing; the barman was serving others with cigarettes, while working the machine. In the end I was given a glass so boiling hot that it had to be sipped slowly, with care. I drank it with indifference, brushing the flies away, my back to the unemployed men.

Dongiovanni, too, the fisherman on land, took no notice of them. He continued to lean on the counter, deep in thought; and I went on sipping my coffee, with an occasional glance at the mirror behind the bottles, pretending not to recognize Dongiovanni.

Someone came in, and went out again. Dongiovanni slipped cautiously towards the end of the counter nearest to me, between me and the door. For a moment he bent towards me and whispered suddenly in my ear: "Papa wants your skin." Again he leant in my direction, like a friend revealing a secret: "Remember me. I have warned you. Look out for Papa."

When I passed his sturdy back to go out again, he neither followed me nor moved a finger. He did not even come to the threshold to look at my car as it set off rapidly for the factory.

In my office, Di Marzo, whom I had sent for in the morning was waiting. Finding him already there, I owed him my full attention, for he is an intelligent young man, who only suffers from melancholia.

In the factory he feels isolated, he feels different.

"In what way different?" I asked, trying to push the thought of Dongiovanni further from my mind.

"Different."

"Do you feel different at home, too?" His eyes lit up. Yes, even at home, he suffered from the same sense of being different from others.

"Are you lonely?"

"Not really lonely, Doctor."

"Who do you live with?"

"With my sister, my brother-in-law . . ."

"Have they children?"

"Five."

"Would you be happier in your own house?"

"Yes, Doctor. I am alone, I'm the sort to live alone in a house that belongs to me." He was gazing at me with his grey eyes, beneath the high, romantic forehead of a neurotic. But at Santa Maria . . . to live alone in Santa Maria, in a bachelor apartment . . . He knew the answer only too well.

Just because he is so reasonable there is nothing apparently against him, except himself; he works well, earns well, is thought well of by his superiors. His malady is too impalpable for life in a factory.

I sighed. "Di Marzo . . ."

He was waiting, though with a shy and sceptical air, for me to speak.

"We must see one another again . . . it is no use speaking just once about these things . . . We must become friends."

"Yes, Doctor."

Just because I wanted to see him again, and often, I had cut off the interview too hurriedly. But then, would it really help him to let him understand that I could sympathize because I, too, shared his subtle malady, but for this very reason knew the difficulty of curing it?

It was late, and dark. Once more night falls again at closing time, and the lights of the cars dazzle the carabineer and Bellomo as we pass; then the asphalt surface of the road glitters between two walls of darkness along the familar way. I arrived home without being aware of a line of thought at the back of my mind.

It would be easy for Papa to take me by surprise, but how? With a revolver shot? A cudgel? A beam laid across the road? Yet it seemed to me that he was fundamentally a good-natured man. In any case I kept my face low over the steering-wheel and away from the window, to avoid some imaginary blow.

I entered my house, to find that Dattilo had just been there to warn my wife that Dongiovanni wanted to kill me.

CHAPTER XIX

Saturday morning

Yesterday evening after I had left, towards seven o'clock, a bomb was thrown a few feet from the black car of one of the engineers. "Have you heard the news?" the Signorina asked as I entered my office, and for the moment I feared that an accident had happened to Di Marzo.

The car had been leaving the gates with the engineer at the wheel and two clerical workers to whom he was giving a lift; it had taken the curve to the left and was accelerating on the main road. A blaze of light appeared in front of the radiator a moment before the car would have passed over it. The engineer braked violently, and a little further on a shadow disappeared over the wall.

Leaving the car, the engineer went in pursuit: he found himself on a slippery, earthen slope, near a drop of some fifty feet into the dark, at the cliff's edge. Behind this famous wall are two precipitous paths that lead down to the lower road, by way of the cliffs where Dongiovanni, Accettura and others have their dwellings, never visited by us. Two paths difficult to negotiate even by day.

There was no one there. The cardboard dynamiter—perhaps his bomb was of cardboard—knew his way, otherwise he would have broken his neck. The engineer peered into the night, convinced that only an old inhabitant of the place and one who had become attached to the pavement and the porters' lodge, could have conceived the idea of hiding himself there, of throwing his species of infernal machine and then escaping by way of the precipice. He returned to the factory—the Manager was still in his office—and telephoned to the carabineers. Our own carabineer had not fired a shot. The engineer then proceeded on his way to the city.

On the asphalt a small hole and a grey patch indicated the place of the explosion, and behind the wall there were traces of footsteps and some displaced earth. For the first time I crossed this horizon of the wall where they sat and waited all day, and found a hidden world of steep rocky slopes and prickly pears, still high up but much nearer the sea than we are here. One almost felt suspended above it.

In the meantime it was being said in the factory that if the bomb —however amateurishly made—had exploded beneath the petrol tank of the car, the whole thing would have gone up in flames.

However, all is quiet in the factory, since the bomb is a matter concerning only the management and those, like the Signorina and myself, whose job it is to waste time over the problems of the porters' lodge, and who know all the trouble-makers around it. We had at once thought it must be Donnarumma: not Dongiovanni, or Papa, despite the recent threats, nor any one of our workers. As to Dattilo, he had a perfect alibi, because he was at my house, with my wife.

This morning, in the entrance hall, the production-manager, a cool-headed engineer, was laughing about the attempt: he said it was nothing to make a fuss about and we must go on with our work. If anyone congratulated him on a danger escaped, he looked puzzled and enquired: "What danger?" But the Signorina and I are not as detached as the technicians: we do not know whether to nourish fear or courage, if courage does not consist in having the foresight to take precautionary measures.

Monday

Yesterday the Manager was rung up at his house by an anonymous caller who informed him that there had been a mistake: the bomb was intended for him.

Since his car, too, is a black one, and on Friday he was late in leaving the works, the man must have miscalculated or lost patience. By telephoning to point out the real aim of the attempt he, or some confederate, seemed to think he was putting things right and at any rate reaching the intended victim morally, though retrospectively.

The Manager would be the most likely victim of a rejected applicant, as we had at once suspected; while the engineer might have aroused the hatred of one of our employees. After the telephone message, although the author of the attempt was no nearer identification, his aim, at least, was clear, and the shadow of a suspicion that the culprit might have been one of our own people was removed.

Not a single mention of the bomb by the workers has been overheard. Straniero and the whole of the works committee are silent. The others either did not know of the incident or are quite indifferent.

On these occasions there is an understanding on all sides that such an occurrence is to be regarded as out of the ordinary, an odd episode that has just happened to touch our lives but which it would be cowardly to take as either symptomatic or alarming. For me, too, and for the Signorina, it is odd and out of the ordinary; yet to us it seems that we have seen not only its birth but its growth, and we have a feeling that more importance should be attached to it, and to our opinion. For us it is a serious matter, such as the cracking of a press would be to the engineers. Furthermore, although the bomb was not thrown at us we feel it was ours, and we have a certain sense of offended pride in the fact that we are considered worthy of threats but not, for hierarchical reasons, of their execution.

And we are still uncertain: is it better to over-rate or under-rate its importance? Ought we to take defensive action or expose ourselves defiantly to danger? The former might be cowardly, the latter fool-hardy; but if the factory's attitude is to be one of indifference, it is not for us to spread anxiety. It is the factory that decrees our reaction.

This morning the city newspapers of the Right inveigh against the ingratitude of those we are benefiting. The Communist *Unità* retorts: "As to the person who is supposed to have thrown the infernal machine, and whom the newspaper in question insists on regarding as one of the applicants whose name appears on the list of new candidates for engagement, it is thought not impossible by the Carabineers that he does not exist, and that the little petard or squib, left by some child on the road, exploded because the engineer passed over it at high speed."

With the paper in my hand I went straight to Amoruso in the peaceful though noisy workshop. Such a distortion of the truth could only harm those whom it was designed to defend. Amoruso was work-ing quietly. He, too, seemed hardly able to remember the bomb—or was he pretending? Yes, he had seen something in his paper . . .

"But this article? Amoruso, do children leave explosives on the road? And our cars have to go slowly at the gates, we all know they do . . ." He was surprised rather than embarrassed. "Amoruso, after all it is not carnival time, no one is letting off fireworks. Why don't they explain instead that we can only engage one in a thousand, that this is the real cause?" "Doctor . . ." "Do you believe in the child and the squib?" "Doctor, it's only the newspapers . . . You know how they go on. They're always in a hurry. They write here and are pro-bably printed in Rome, they arrange things anyhow, by telephone."

He was neither ashamed nor afraid. Indeed, the absurdity of his party paper left him unmoved. He was ready to justify it. But a subtle, dignified look of perplexity became stamped on his face, to cover his political defence and his own silence.

Tuesday

The workers will have nothing to do with it. They leave the matter to the Carabineers and the management, as a private affair of the authorities, or, at most, of the clerical staff; an incident that has cropped up between a madman and the employers.

According to the Carabineers, it is possible that the footprints on the freshly turned earth beyond the wall correspond to the dilapidated shoes of Donnarumma.

One inevitably suspects Donnarumma, but it is not impossible that this apparent clue is an effect, not the cause, of our suspicions. Who wants to persecute Donnarumma in these days? Yet blind violence is exactly what one reads in his eyes.

Other anonymous telephone calls to the Manager's house insist on the mistake. "It was for you, it was for you."

Wednesday

They have arrested Donnarumma, not for the attempt, since no proof exists, but on account of his past threats.

We fail to follow the technique of justice; do the footprints, then, not correspond to his shoes? Is there a culprit or is there need of a culprit?

The Lieutenant of Carabineers came to see us; calm and vague in manner, he let it be understood that he was going to deal, himself, with Donnarumma and some others in the barracks, and that we must not interfere. The culprit was his by right. He would come back and question us in due course.

The Signorina and I have the impression that we alone really mind: we are apprehensive, indignant, mistrustful: sentiments that perhaps the only one to share with equal intensity is Donnarumma, who at this moment, is closer to us than anyone else.

Tuesday

A week has passed, but there is nothing fresh to report. The episode must therefore be regarded as closed and it would not be opportune for anyone to resuscitate or try to clear it up. Our fair factory, in all its pride and freedom, continues with production, having as it were shaken this nuisance from its back.

In the afternoon the officer of Carabineers reappeared, to question us briefly. He was afraid we were wasting time. I did not explicitly accuse Donnarumma; I only explained that of the hundreds of persons who had been interviewed by me, and of all those who hang about the porters' lodge, or my own house, or along the main road to Santa Maria and in the caves, one only had stony hatred depicted on his face, a smouldering fire in his eyes. One only.

Wednesday

The bomb has created a void round the gates and round me; that small explosion now keeps them all at a distance, Dattilo and Accettura, Dongiovanni and Papaleo; and the new applicants come to ask for an interview with a slight air of embarrassment.

Dongiovanni's and Papa's fire has been stolen: now that a bomb has been exploded they cannot go on with their threats of slaughter.

The Signorina and I can tranquilly proceed with the examinations.

Friday

Donnarumma has been condemned to prison for two weeks for threatening behaviour.

The Signorina and I can imagine his fury: not when he starts his sentence, but when he comes out and returns to the gates.

Meanwhile, the police are assisting the Carabineers in their still mysterious investigations, and are following quite a different trail from that of the latter. The incident is becoming absorbed into the human labyrinth of Santa Maria.

We now have both a carabineer and a policeman at our gates.

CHAPTER XX

ON SUNDAY THERE was another *festa*, the most official and memorable that we have had; almost a consecration of the factory. The great Central and Southern Industrial Association was visiting us. At ten in the morning a chosen number of our staff were ranged under the portico to receive the guests, all alert and smartly dressed, though feigning among themselves a slight air of boredom at being used as the factory's representatives on a social occasion. From the coaches and cars a crowd of business-men, of elegant wives, some with children, poured out, while the Manager came forward to organize them into groups for visiting the premises. Each group was entrusted to one of us. We had all been chosen for this purpose, and we all felt on an equality: members of the works committee, technical experts, accountants and engineers.

Those who had affected contempt for this day of glory for the firm, in order to stay at home, or who were not chosen, must have been nursing envy in their hearts.

Some of the members' daughters looked very charming as they stepped lightly from the cars and there was much competition among the *ciceroni* to capture the groups that included them. Even the Manager, despite his official air in his grey suit, lent himself to this manœuvre; and the production-manager, too, unexpectedly showed himself not above it. Perhaps the most serious were Amoruso and Straniero.

Being kept in reserve for latecomers, I saw almost everyone arrive. Talkative and full of interest, industrialists, professional men and important people of all kinds, with their wives, thronged the covered way leading from the entrance. The carabineer and the policeman were cheerfully doing their share of the honours, and for the time being the territory once occupied by Donnarumma, Chiodo and Papaleo was taken over by the flower of the higher, professional classes.

In charge of three men, a lady and a young girl, I led the way first to the social welfare wing. They were in no hurry, and I kept looking at my watch, as I tried to urge them on. My interest in the factory itself was greater than theirs. We visited all the white-tiled rooms, the oculist's consulting-room, the sick-room, the radiant heat department and the rooms where anti-rheumatic heat treatment and injections are given. The lady and her daughter gave great attention to the equipment of this section, like two Red Cross nurses visiting a hospital. The men were more interested in the first-aid room, and were fascinated by the two beds, ready prepared, with their soft pillows. At this rate we were going to be late for the final appointment. I had to beg them to follow me, but the girl was drawn away by the library and it seemed that we should have to spend the morning among the books and weeklies.

When we left the library I walked them quickly along the corridor towards the cement stairs leading to the production wing. Halfway up the three men began to argue; moreover, one of them was the sort who only succeed in speaking when standing still. He was explaining that we Italians had nothing to learn from the United States. He went on up the steps, then stopped again. When we finally got among the presses, they hardly saw them. A flood of visitors had engulfed the workshops, and confusion reigned amidst the shining machinery. Further on, we began to lose touch with one another. A visiting engineer from another group questioned me about some new mechanical apparatus, of which I knew nothing. When we reached the assembly-lines only the lady and her daughter were still with me; but they were more interested here than in the workshops.

Once we had arrived at the council room, the groups broke up and a great noise of talk supervened. Vermouth was handed round by white-jacketed waiters from the city. The sun was breaking through the morning mist and, freed from their dutiful homage to the organization, the guests were able to enjoy the best part of the visit, on the terrace, with its stupendous view.

In the big dining-hall, where the tables, set with gleaming glass, were decorated with carnations, a banquet was subsequently held.

At the high table, dominating the hall, where the principal guests were seated—delegates, directors and chairmen of companies—the dessert began to circulate and the first toasts were drunk. Each speaker commented on the industrialization of Southern Italy and the many problems entailed. The last to speak, and the most important guest—chairman of the greatest financial board in the South—did not confine himself to thanks and good wishes for a happy future. His was an undertaking of greater scope: that of paying tribute to the ideological principles that animate our factory, our firm, and the President of our firm; in other words, the "impalpable virtue", as he said, enclosed within these walls.

Although a man of subtle intelligence and practical achievement, his phrases became more and more involved as he plunged deeper into his subject, and he had to have recourse to all the tricks of traditional oratory in emphasizing his points. His voice rose and fell with monotonous conviction.

He turned towards our own President, whom I had not seen all day. Only now that he was the object of the speaker's laudatory remarks was I able to pick him out from among the rest, as he sat listening impassively, staring at the table and now and then looking up in sign of thanks.

The speaker said that he appreciated these ideas and principles profoundly, because, politically, they were neither of the Left nor the Right, but drew the best from every side. He tried to drive home this theme. But it was clear that he was speaking—with great courtesy and respect—of ideas and principles of which he knew very little. Great applause followed, and then silence.

Our President rose to his feet and thanked the speakers. His thin, rather mournful voice scarcely reached to the end of the room. Although he had no notes with him, he sounded, as usual, as though he were reading, and spoke unemotionally, without a single gesture; his blue eyes were steady and his phrases came spontaneously to his lips.

He recalled his motives in building the factory down here, stressed its excellent output, and the great abilities of the southern workers; and then indicated the problems that a factory solved, but also created, in a non-industrial area. He said that a factory cannot be an end in itself. It was the men he cared for. Was he, I wondered, now going to reply to the praise he had received for an eclectic political attitude? Slowly he was working up to his general, characteristic ideas, discreetly and almost, it seemed, inadvertently, as though developing a theme in his own mind.

He was saying: ". . . men will find that the essential element in their love for their native land lies in the natural area in which they have spent their infancy; and that the concrete element of human brotherhood must be based on the solidarity that comes from a community of traditions and experiences. The present elementary structure of our society does not determine any such unity of sentiments and therefore renders the setting up of true human solidarity very difficult." His thoughts, still precisely phrased, now seemed to be taking flight into somewhat mystical regions.

He went on: "The joy of work, which today is denied to the majority of workers in modern industry, will finally return when the worker comes to realize that his effort, his labour, his sacrifice—because it will always be sacrifice—is materially and spiritually bound to an entity that is noble and humane, and that he himself is able to understand and appreciate; since his own work serves to make possible that living, effective community, in the place where he and his sons have their lives, their interests and their ties." He underlined nothing by his tone of voice, for it seemed to him that good reasoning was enough; calm, restrained and courteous, he let his thoughts go out to his guests, as they sat at the tables, relaxed and well fed.

He did not raise his voice or move a finger even when, at the close of his speech, he proudly parried a possible objection: "Let no one fear that this new spirit will give rise to a weak or inconsistent humanitarianism; for nothing is stronger and more violent, in just men, than resentment against injustice." And so he ended.

In the late afternoon many of our guests went off by car to visit the picturesque sights in the vicinity. But some preferred to stay and see the factory housing estate. Two or three of the clerical staff were waiting in the drive, towards four o'clock, for a car to take a party to the village, and were talking about the reception.

From the porters' lodge a tall, elegant police officer came striding up the drive, after speaking to his man stationed beside the carabineer at the entrance: he drew me aside, to say: "It wasn't Donnarumma."

I was sorry to hear this, for one reason only. If not Donnarumma, then who could it have been? Had we suspected our only enemy unjustly?

"Who was it then?" I asked, although the subject was hardly suited to the day.

"The footprints do not correspond with Donnarumma's shoes."

"But who, then?"

"It might have been anyone . . . But we, Doctor . . . we shall get him, don't you trouble yourselves about it. It's a fine fish that we're about to hook. We've been playing it, so far. You must give us time."

"Give the police time? How long?"

"We have our special lines of approach and we shall soon close in on our man. Donnarumma is a marvel, but it wasn't him. Everything takes time, down here. Be patient." He went down to the entrance again without saying more.

The Sunday evening was slowly drawing in over the countryside and the houses of Santa Maria. The celebrations at the factory had left the teeming little town untouched, though excited and curious. If

there were a great many of us here today, important people who had
come from afar, there were still more people in Santa Maria, who had
been there much longer. Some animation was to be seen at the entrance
to the housing estate, which was full of cars, and those of the visitors
who were keenest to see all they could were walking about the paths
and courtyards; while a fringe of indigenous spectators watched from
the road, and the families in the houses were flustered by continual
visits.

From the balcony stairway of one of the houses issued a young man,
one of our guests, carrying a leather brief-case under his arm; with the
vigour of youth, he had the air of a middle-aged man. He greeted me
warmly and familiarly, though he had forgotten my name and I did
not remember his. But he was, in fact, a former school-fellow of mine.

Being an engineer, he was now in charge of a factory, and as such
had been invited today. We exchanged reminiscences, and each gave a
rapid account of our post-school careers, for we had not met meanwhile, since I had not studied engineering. I explained about the
personnel office. "Psychotechnology?" he said at once.

"My job is that of selecting the men."

He became excited at this. "Selecting the men." He looked at me
with a strange intensity. "Ah, I direct a factory, and it's the picking out
of the right men to engage that interests me more than anything else.
How do you go about it?"

I briefly described our methods and the laboratory. Would he like
to see it? I could open it for him.

He was impatient, but not to go and see the laboratory; impatient
about something else. He listened sceptically to me, as I described the
interviews; and shook his head, with a look of irritation, as he repeated:
"Ah, selecting the right men, that's the problem." To content him I
went on to express doubts on the efficacy of the interviews, and also on
the statistics of the tests, since this might be of greater interest to an
engineer. By now he was not so much sceptical as dissatisfied.

"But tell me," he demanded, "how do you do the real sifting?"

"Like that . . . As I have been explaining." He looked at me again
and pursed his lips. Perhaps, I thought, this ability of ours to choose
our men offended him; his own factory might be in a state of crisis.
Out of courtesy I said, undervaluing our work: "Of course, we have to
take on men. It's no merit of ours. We've a new factory to staff."

"I am doubling my departments," he said quickly, with the voice
of the pupil turned master. "But who should one take on? In short,
whom do you choose?"

"The best . . . I know, it's not easy to pick the best. We make mistakes. We often make mistakes. Psychology isn't an infallible guide. And we have tragic pressure at our doors." He was not interested. With a frustrated air he took hold of the lapel of my jacket and gave me a knowing smile: "But, in short, to keep out the Communists . . . You know perfectly well that in engaging personnel that's all that counts. How do you discover which of them are Communists?"

"We don't discover them."

But he was not to be contented with that. As we walked round the village, he told me what a life the Reds led him in his engineering works; they were a perfect curse; his wife, in the evenings, wept over the Communists. Amoruso passed us, with a friendly greeting, and went into his house. My friend asked who he was and why he had such a good house.

Could he be made to believe that the Communist representative on the works committee had been assigned one of these special houses?

I took him to see Amoruso.

Amoruso, surprised in his own residence, introduced his family and offered us vermouth. My erstwhile school-friend began to ask questions, and, scrutinizing him intently, listened with astonishment to his replies. We came to the question of wages. Amoruso does not earn much more than he needs for a livelihood, but nevertheless the figure he mentioned was one to strike the young factory manager dumb with amazement.

Saturday

Numerous requests for work have come in as a result of our celebrations this week. Every event of the kind is interpreted locally as a sign of the factory's expansion; furthermore, it is thought that in the wake of a *festa* the personnel office must be in an optimistic, tolerant mood.

The entrance is crowded again, but the applicants are disciplined and patient, for the former ring-leaders are missing.

They will think that the psychologist is leaving out of fear of Donnarumma. And in fact, I am going away today.

End of November—Milan

The last report sent in by the works committee raised the question of the rate-fixing and the different categories of piece-work. I discussed this matter with the Manager.

The time-intervals must be linked to the methods of work. Each part must, in a given time, be executed by a given method, that is, with movements laid down beforehand. Every worker would instinctively like to arrange things himself, and to invent his own sequence of movements, but the rate-fixer assigns him the time and shows him how to achieve it; how to manœuvre the tool and how, and in what order, to move his hands and feet. The worker feels that this constriction slows him up, and believes that, if he were left alone to improvise as he thinks best, he would be quicker; in other words, he wants freedom of action. But time and motion study has its own reasons and its own justification implicit in the method, which is fixed. It is always difficult and dangerous to persuade men that the renunciation of liberty may benefit themselves.

Similarly, some workers prefer to risk an accident rather than train themselves to use methods of protection that at first hamper them.

Piece-work categories apply to the job rather than to the man; and these objective valuations make the difficulties of the labour force understandable, and should award them just treatment. But theoretically a man has no fixed value, in himself; he acquires different values in changing his job; and he therefore may fall, as well as rise. Yet even if a man's path of progress is guaranteed in one particular direction, that is, upwards, towards improvement, he clings to his own subjective value. He refuses to accept the necessity, the reasonableness of an analysis of the jobs he has had, and does not believe in our attempt at order. He only asks for analysis and improvement in his own category, that is, of himself, and he is ready to fight for it. This was my last conversation with the Manager: it affected the factory's future and the effort not to leave it to itself. But, in this effort, the workers and the management inevitably come into conflict. We became vague. We suddenly realized that that afternoon was my last and did not know how to look at one another. I had already said good-bye to everyone else.

My departure took place the next day from the railway station, after leaving the little house above the sea for ever.

On my way to the city I tried to imprint the road, the olive-trees, the hills, on my mind, in order to forget nothing of that land and sky. In the same way, on the previous day, I had looked at every corner of the factory, as one does in leaving a much-loved room, before going out and shutting the door upon it.

At the station, there were only ten minutes in hand before the train was due to start. I had stopped along the road to gaze at the sea, knowing that I would never again work on the coast. Now I was crossing the piazza to the solitary, distinguished-looking railway station.

Two big black cars, full of armed police, shot across the piazza in the direction of the coast-road. Were they going to the factory? What had happened? Donnarumma must have returned to the attack. Some unforeseeable discontent, a real revolt, that had been smouldering for months without anyone being aware of it, must have broken out today, this very day. I must telephone at once; I must return, if something had happened; I must begin again at the beginning, glad to be forced not to leave.

I found a telephone, but I lost my train. Since it was the lunch-hour, no one was at the factory's switchboard, the telephonist being in the dining-hall and the external line connected with the entrance. It rang and rang; no answer; Bellomo must be out of his box: was he waiting in the road for the police?

At last I heard his always rather breathless voice. After so many affecting farewells he was now alarmed at the psychologist's continued presence. "Yes. Yes, Doctor," he was saying, confusedly, like someone woken up in the middle of the night.

"It's nothing, Bellomo, really. I saw two police cars going out towards the factory . . ."

"What did you say, Doctor?"

"Has anything happened, Bellomo? There were two black cars. I wanted to know if everything was quiet at the factory."

"All quiet here, Doctor, at your service," said Bellomo, with his sentry's voice. "There's only Dattilo about, looking for you."

"You see . . . I thought the police . . ."

"No police here, Doctor," he protested, indignantly.

"Good-bye, Bellomo, good-bye."

At that hour the workers were out on the grass, in the sunshine, waiting for the bell; it was the quietest, laziest moment of the day. Only Dattilo, the most pacific and tenacious of them all, still lingered at the entrance: still waiting to marry.

I went down to the port, crowded, as ever, with boats, and sat on some steps on the jetty, while waiting for the next train. Why could not one live at Santa Maria for ever?

Next day the newspapers reported a crime committed far away in the countryside beyond the factory. A crime that had no connection with industry.

1955–1957